# Notes on Compass Work

## Kemp & Yo

Stanford Maritime Limited
Member Company of the George Philip Group
12-14 Long Acre London WC2E 9LP

First published 1962
Second edition 1972

Reprinted 1974, 1977, 1979, 1984
© John F. Kemp 1962, 1972

Printed in Great Britain by
Robert Hartnoll Ltd.,
Bodmin, Cornwall

ISBN 0 540 00362 x

## STANFORD MARITIME LONDON

# CONTENTS

## PREFACE

This book has been written primarily to cover the Magnetic and Gyro Compass syllabus for the Board of Trade examination for a Master's Certificate of Competency. At the same time those studying for a First Mate's Certificate will find the section on the gyro compass extremely useful.

The concise presentation of the subject matter has been made possible by reducing the work to its simplest terms. We have achieved this by omitting any unnecessary mathematics or mathematical concepts. A large number of diagrams illustrate the various points made in the text.

The section of worked examples will be found useful in furthering the reader's knowledge of the subject and rapid reference to the substance of each example can be made in the index.

Our thanks are due to all those who have assisted in the preparation of this book. In particular we are indebted to Messrs. H. Browne (Depot) Ltd., and also to Messrs. S.G. Brown Ltd., by whose kind permission the illustrations on pages 18 and 20 are reproduced.

KENLEY, SURREY.
September 1962

J. F. KEMP
PETER YOUNG

## PREFACE TO REVISED EDITION

A new edition of this book has become necessary because of the change from the C.G.S. to the S.I. system of units. Also to meet the requirements of new syllabuses for professional examinations, the treatment of the magnetic compass has been modified and additional material has been included.

January, 1972

J. F. KEMP
PETER YOUNG.

# 1. The Gyroscopic Compass

**A Gyroscope** consists basically of a spinning wheel. Its important inherent properties are gyroscopic inertia and precession. If a spinning wheel is free to turn about two axes at right angles to each other and to the spin axis, it is said to be a free gyroscope.

**A free gyroscope**, when spinning rapidly, possesses considerable directional stability or inertia, i.e. it has a great resistance to any tendency to change the direction in which its spin axis lies. The Earth approximates to a free gyroscope and its spin axis does in fact lie in a direction (pointing towards the pole star) which remains nearly constant in space.

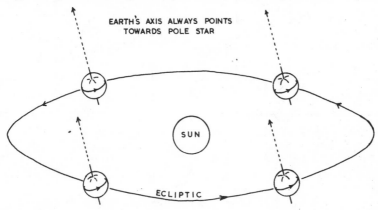

EARTH'S AXIS ALWAYS POINTS TOWARDS POLE STAR

SUN

ECLIPTIC

A spinning wheel can be made to approximate to a free gyroscope by supporting the spin axis in gimbals, as illustrated below, so that the centre of gravity of the wheel lies at the level of the gimbal axes and so that the pivots are made as frictionless as possible. The axis of such a gyroscope tends to point to a fixed direction in space. Although there is no movement in space, the axis of a free gyroscope can have an apparent movement due to the rotation of the Earth. This movement may be conveniently visualized if it is imagined that the gyroscope axis in its initial position is pointing towards a fixed star, i.e. towards a fixed point in space. The apparent motion of the gyroscope will then be to follow the apparent motion of the star as the Earth rotates.

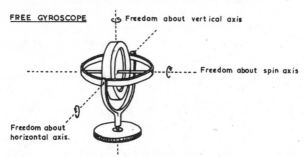

FREE GYROSCOPE   Freedom about vertical axis

Freedom about spin axis

Freedom about horizontal axis.

**Tilt.** If a free gyroscope is situated on the Equator and lies with its axis East-West and horizontal it can be thought of as pointing to a star which has zero declination and is about to rise. The East end of the gyroscope axis will follow the movement of this star and will tilt upwards as the star rises. After nearly six hours the axis will be vertical and after nearly twelve hours the gyroscope will have turned completely over with the axis again horizontal and the original East end of the axis pointing to the star setting due West. After one sidereal day (23h. 56m.) the gyroscope will have tilted through 360° and the hypothetical star will again be rising. This rate of tilting, 360° in nearly 24 hours, is a rate of 15° per hour.

AT EQUATOR E.- W.

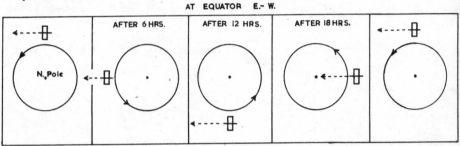

If the gyroscope had been situated on the equator with its axis lying North-South, the North end would be pointing towards the Pole Star and would then have no apparent movement relative to the Earth. The rate of tilting thus varies from zero when the axis is lying North-South to a maximum when it is lying East-West, i.e. rate of tilting varies as the sine of the azimuth.

AT EQUATOR N.-S.

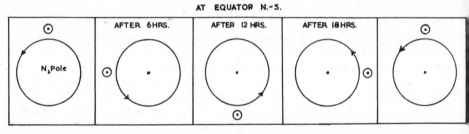

A free gyroscope situated at a pole with its axis horizontal would have an apparent turntable motion due to the Earth's rotation, i.e. it would follow a fixed star around the horizon but it would not rise or set. The rate of tilting thus varies from a maximum when the latitude is 0° to zero when the latitude is 90°, i.e. rate of tilting varies as the cosine of the latitude.

AT POLE HORIZONTAL

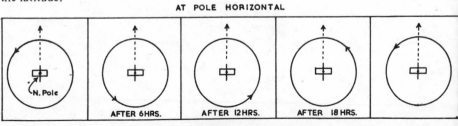

The following formula gives the rate of tilting of a free gyroscope at any instant, but it must be borne in mind that the rate is constantly changing and the value given by the formula cannot be taken as constant over a considerable period of time.

Rate of Tilting in degrees per hour = 15° sin Azimuth cos Latitude.

The direction of tilting is such that the end of the gyro axis which lies to the East of the meridian tilts upwards and the end which lies to the West of the meridian tilts downwards.

**Drift** is the apparent movement of a gyroscope in azimuth. A free gyroscope situated at the North Pole with its axis horizontal will have an apparent movement which is entirely in the horizontal plane. Its axis will appear to move in a clockwise direction when viewed from above due to the real counter-clockwise rotation of the Earth beneath. This "turntable" motion causes the gyroscope to drift through 360° in nearly 24 hours, i.e. at a rate of 15° per hour.

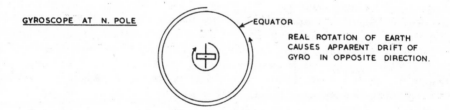

GYROSCOPE AT N. POLE                    EQUATOR

REAL ROTATION OF EARTH
CAUSES APPARENT DRIFT OF
GYRO IN OPPOSITE DIRECTION.

A free gyroscope situated at the equator with its axis horizontal will not drift at all, irrespective of whether its axis is set in the North-South or East-West line. The rate of drift for a gyroscope with its axis horizontal thus varies from a maximum at the poles to zero at the equator, i.e. rate of drift varies as the sine of the latitude. For a gyroscope with its axis horizontal:-

Rate of Drift in degrees per hour = 15° sin Latitude.

The direction of drift depends upon hemisphere so that the North end of a horizontal gyro axis drifts to the eastwards in the northern hemisphere but to the westwards in the southern hemisphere.

**Combined tilt and drift.** At a latitude intermediate between the equator and a pole, the apparent motion of a free gyroscope consists partly of tilt and partly of drift. The motion can be predicted by referring to a star diagram on the plane of the rational horizon as used for illustrating navigational problems. Thus if a free gyroscope in latitude 50°N. is set with its spin axis East-West and horizontal its apparent movement may be predicted by considering the diagram below.

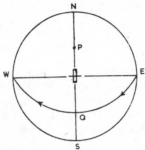

The gyroscope, with its axis horizontal, has the East end of its axis pointing to a star which is just rising at the East point of the horizon (E. in the diagram). Such a star is clearly on the equinoctial and has a declination of zero, so that its path will be along the equinoctial (EQW in the diagram). The East end of the gyroscope axis will commence to tilt upwards as the star rises in altitude and will drift towards the South point of the horizon as the star changes its position in azimuth. After nearly six hours the axis will be pointing at the star at Q so that axis will lie in the North-South line with its South end tilted 40° above the horizon. Thereafter the South end of the axis will drift towards the West point of the horizon and will tilt downwards until after a further six hours the axis will again be horizontal with the original East end directed towards the West point of the horizon where the star is just setting. During the following twelve hours the gyroscope axis will tilt below the horizon until one sidereal day after the original observation the star will again be about to rise at the East point of the horizon and the gyroscope will have returned to its starting point.

As a second example we may consider the case of a free gyroscope set with its axis North-South and horizontal at a position in latitude 30° North. A star in the direction to which the North end of the axis points is circumpolar and will have an apparent motion along its circle of declination (shown as a pecked line in the diagram below).

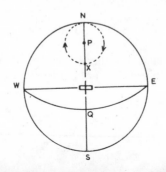

The North end of the gyroscope axis will of course follow the apparent motion of the star, the drift being initially towards the East and the maximum tilt occurring after half a sidereal day when the star is at position X.

In general the axis of a free gyroscope will describe a circle round the elevated pole corresponding to the circle of declination of a star. The circle may lie entirely above the horizon as in the last example or it may lie partly below the horizon as in the first example.

**Precession.** If a torque (a turning moment) in the plane of the spinning wheel is applied to a gyroscope axis, the effect is only to increase or decrease the rate of spin; the direction in which the spin axis lies is unaffected. If a torque is applied to a gyroscope axis in a plane at right angles to the plane of spin the gyroscope becomes unbalanced and to restore the balance it moves in a direction at right angles both to the plane of the spinning wheel and the plane in which the torque is applied. This movement at right angles to the torque is known as precession and a balance is achieved in much the same way that a weight swung in a circle on the end of a string achieves a balance by virtue of its movement at right angles to the string although the force acting on the weight is along the length of the string.

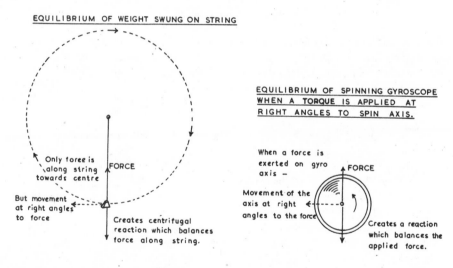

EQUILIBRIUM OF WEIGHT SWUNG ON STRING

Only foree is along string towards centre

FORCE

But movement at right angles to force

Creates centrifugal reaction which balances force along string.

EQUILIBRIUM OF SPINNING GYROSCOPE WHEN A TORQUE IS APPLIED AT RIGHT ANGLES TO SPIN AXIS.

When a force is exerted on gyro axis —

Movement of the axis at right angles to the force

FORCE

Creates a reaction which balances the applied force.

The direction in which a gyroscope axis moves when a force is applied to it depends upon the direction in which the wheel is spinning. The direction of the precession due to a particular torque may be predicted by imagining an arrow pasted on the gyroscope wheel so as to indicate the direction of the force which causes the torque. If the gyroscope wheel is then turned through 90° in the direction of spin, the new position of the arrow will indicate the direction in which the gyroscope must precess in order to balance the applied torque.

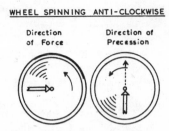

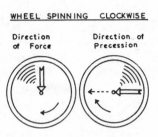

The rate at which a gyroscope precesses depends upon the weight of the gyroscope wheel and the way in which the weight is distributed with respect to the axis, i.e. upon the moment of inertia (I) of the wheel. The greater the moment of inertia, the slower will be the rate of precession. The greater the torque (T) applied to the gyroscope axis, the greater the rate of precession. The faster the rate at which the wheel spins (S), the greater will be its momentum and the slower will be the rate of precession. Combining these three factors we arrive at a formula as follows:-

$$\text{Rate of Precession} = \frac{T}{S.I.}$$

**Gravity control.** A gyroscope suspended freely in gimbals may be made North-seeking by attaching a weight to the rotor casing either above or below the centre of gravity of the rotor so that when the axis lies horizontal the weight is distributed equally between the two ends of the axis but when the gyroscope is tilted the weight exerts more thrust on one end of the axis than on the other. This causes a torque in a vertical plane and the gyroscope axis is made to precess horizontally.

When one end of a gyroscope axis is to the East of the true meridian it it pointing at a rising star and will always tilt upwards. To cause this end to precess towards the North if the gyroscope wheel is spinning clockwise when viewed from the West a downwards force is required on the East end of the axis. This effect can be provided, when the East end of the axis tilts upwards by suspending a control weight below the gyroscope, thus making the rotor casing "bottom heavy".

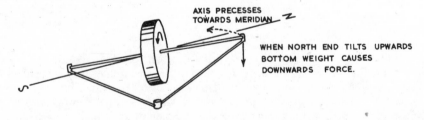

To cause the East end of the axis to precess towards the North if the gyroscope rotor is spinning anti-clockwise when viewed from the West, a downwards force is required on the West end of the axis. This effect can be provided when the East end of the axis tilts upwards, by supporting the control weight above the gyroscope, thus making the rotor casing "top heavy".

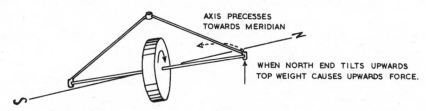

AXIS PRECESSES TOWARDS MERIDIAN

WHEN NORTH END TILTS UPWARDS TOP WEIGHT CAUSES UPWARDS FORCE.

A gyroscope with gravity control as described above will not settle in the meridian but the North-seeking end of the axis will tend to precess towards the meridian when it lies East of North and tilted upwards. It is left as an exercise for the student to verify that it will also tend to precess towards the meridian when the North-seeking end of the axis lies to the West of North and is tilted downwards.

In an intermediate North latitude, a free gyroscope set with its axis North-South and horizontal has an apparent motion such that the North end of its axis describes a circle round the celestial pole. The projection of such a circle on a vertical plane to the North-ward of the gyroscope position is illustrated as the firm line in the diagram below.

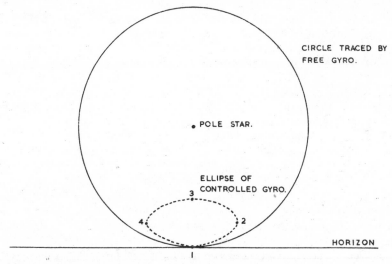

CIRCLE TRACED BY FREE GYRO.

• POLE STAR.

ELLIPSE OF CONTROLLED GYRO.

HORIZON

The North-seeking end of the axis of a gravity controlled gyroscope, started in a similar position will trace out an elliptical path as illustrated by a pecked line in the figure above. At position (1) with the gyroscope axis horizontal the gravity control has no effect; the

North end of the axis drifts Eastwards and tilts upwards, initially at the same rate as the free gyroscope. When the North end of the axis has tilted above the horizontal the gravity control causes precession towards the West. This effect at first is not as great as the natural drift towards the East and merely slows the Easterly movement, but later (at position 2) the rate of precession becomes equal and opposite to the rate of drift and thereafter, as the axis continues to tilt upwards, the axis moves towards the West. All the time the axis lies to the East of the meridian, the axis is tilting upwards so that the greatest tilt, and hence the greatest rate of precession, occurs when the gyroscope axis has returned to the meridian (3). Once the North end of the axis has precessed to the West of the meridian the rotation of the Earth causes it to tilt downwards and the rate of precession decreases until at position (4) the rate of precession is again equal and opposite to the rate of drift. Thereafter the axis moves Easterly with a continuing decrease in tilt until the axis again crosses the meridian at its original starting position.

The time taken for a gyroscope axis to trace out a complete ellipse depends on the degree of control which is provided, but it will always be less than the sidereal day which is required for a complete circle of a free gyroscope. The period of commercial gyroscope compasses is often chosen as 84 minutes.

The size and proportions of the ellipse depend upon the starting position of the the gyroscope and the degree of control. In practice the gravity control is such that the ratio of the major axis of the ellipse to the minor axis is very large, i.e. the ellipse is very wide in proportion to its depth. For diagrammatic clarity the ellipses illustrated have their height exaggerated.

**Damping.** In order to respond to the drift, tilt and precession which makes it North-seeking, the suspension of a gyroscope must be virtually frictionless and a gravity controlled gyroscope as described above would then oscillate indefinitely on either side of the meridian. In order that the oscillation shall become smaller with each cycle so that the gyroscope axis finally settles in the meridian, some form of damping other than by friction is needed.

Damping in tilt means that when the North seeking end of the gyroscope axis is tilted a damping torque is applied in a horizontal plane in such a direction that the resultant precession in a vertical plane causes the tilt of the axis to decrease. As the tilt of the gyroscope is decreased so the precession in azimuth becomes progressively less and the gyroscope spirals in from its starting position to a final settling position as illustrated on page 14.

The Sperry Mk.XIV compass described on page 13 and the Arma-Brown compass described on page 24 are examples of compasses damped in tilt.

Damping in azimuth is achieved by introducing a torque in a vertical plane which causes a precession opposite to the gravity control precession but out of phase with it, i.e. with a time delay. The resultant precession in a horizontal plane causes the axis to overshoot the meridian less each time it crosses it until the gyroscope axis reaches its settling position. The Brown compass is damped in azimuth; it is described in more detail on page 19.

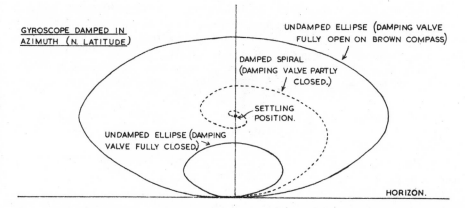

**Course, latitude and speed error** (Northerly speed error). A gyro compass is made north-seeking by a gravity control device which senses any tilting of the gyro axis due to the Earth's rotation. If the axis lies out of the meridian the end which points to the East is sensed to be tilting upwards and the end which lies to the West is sensed to be tilting downwards. The gravity control precesses the gyro axis to seek a position in which the rate of tilting is zero.

The rate of tilting due to the Earth's rotation varies as the sine of the azimuth and is therefore zero when the gyro axis lies in the plane of the meridian.

Course, latitude and speed error arises because a gyro axis is also caused to tilt by the velocity of a ship over the surface of the Earth. The East-West component of a ship's velocity simply adds to or subtracts from the effect of the Earth's rotation, and acts in the same plane. The North-South component of a ship's velocity causes tilting in a plane at right angles to that caused by the earth's rotation. The gyro axis is tilted at a rate (in minutes of arc per hour) which is equal to the North-South component of a ship's speed in knots.

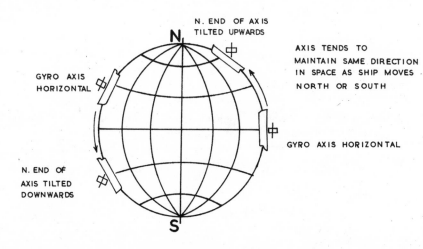

The diagram on page 11 shows that if a ship is on a northerly course the North end of the gyro axis is tilted upwards. The control system, being unable to distinguish between tilting due to the ship's velocity and that due to the Earth's rotation, precesses the North end of the gyro axis to the West, causing an error of this name (i.e. West). For a ship on a southerly course, the North end of the gyro axis is tilted downwards by the ship's velocity and the control system precesses the North end to the East of the meridian.

For a ship heading North or South on a non-rotating Earth a gyro compass, seeking a position in which the rate of tilt was zero, would settle with its axis East West.

In practice the resultant settling position lies between the meridian which it seeks in response to the Earth's rate of tilting (900 cos Lat. minutes of arc per hour) and the East-West line which it seeks in response to the tilting due to the North-South component of a vessel's speed (Speed cos Course in minutes of arc per hour).

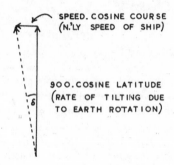

SPEED. COSINE COURSE
(N.'LY SPEED OF SHIP)

900.COSINE LATITUDE
(RATE OF TILTING DUE
TO EARTH ROTATION)

The error $(\delta)$ may be found from a vector triangle as above. Since it is a small angle, it is given in radian measure by:-

$$\delta = \frac{S. \cos Co.}{900 \cos \phi} \qquad [\ S = \text{Speed in Knots}; \phi = \text{Latitude}]$$

or in degrees by:-
$$\delta^\circ = \frac{S. \cos Co.}{900 \cos \phi} \times \frac{180}{\pi}$$

$$\delta^\circ = \frac{S. \cos Co.}{5\pi \cos \phi}$$

In this formula the East-West component of a vessel's velocity is small compared to the rotation of the Earth and is therefore neglected.

The name of the error is westerly for ships on northerly headings and easterly for ships on southerly headings.

## THE SPERRY MK XIV E GYRO COMPASS

This compass is no longer manufactured but many equipments remain in use at sea and its construction illustrates very well the principles of the gyroscopic compass.

The spinning wheel which is the heart of the compass weighs 24 Kg. and rotates at 6,000 revs. per minute. The rotor case is supported in a "vertical ring" by transverse bearings which allow the rotor case to move in tilt. So that the rotor case and the "vertical ring" can move freely together in azimuth, the weight of the "vertical ring", is taken at the top by means of a wire suspension. The wire is hung from a second ring known as the phantom ring which is concentric with and fitted outside the "vertical ring". The phantom ring is made to follow every movement of the vertical ring by means of an electrical follow-up system, thus ensuring that no torsion or twisting which would inhibit the movement of the gyroscope comes in the suspension wire. The compass card is attached to the top of the phantom ring. Upper and lower guide bearings are provided to locate the vertical ring inside the phantom, but these bearings take no weight and can be made almost friction-less. The phantom element is supported beneath the compass card by a "spider" element to which is attached a follow-up motor. A transmitter for operating repeater compass cards is attached to a "lubber's ring" so that, when compass headings are corrected for various errors by rotating the lubber's ring, the corrections are automatically transmitted to the repeaters. The lubber's ring and associated corrector mechanisms are supported on the "spider". The "spider" element is supported in gimbals from the binnacle and damping pots are provided fo prevent excessive oscillations building up as the vessel rolls and pitches.

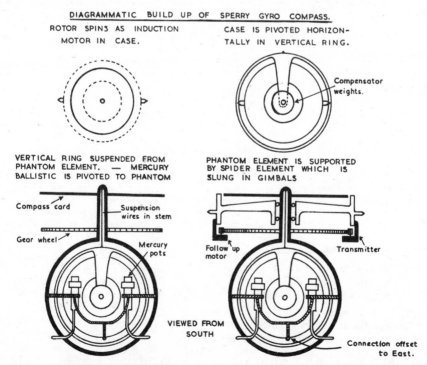

DIAGRAMMATIC  BUILD  UP  OF  SPERRY  GYRO  COMPASS.

ROTOR SPINS AS INDUCTION MOTOR IN CASE.

CASE IS PIVOTED HORIZON-TALLY IN VERTICAL RING.

Compensator weights.

VERTICAL RING SUSPENDED FROM PHANTOM ELEMENT. — MERCURY BALLISTIC IS PIVOTED TO PHANTOM

Compass card
Gear wheel
Suspension wires in stem
Mercury pots

PHANTOM ELEMENT IS SUPPORTED BY SPIDER ELEMENT WHICH IS SLUNG IN GIMBALS

Follow up motor
Transmitter

VIEWED FROM SOUTH

Connection offset to East.

Gravity control is provided by four pots of mercury symmetrically disposed about the compass position and linked together in North-South pairs by small bore pipes. The weight of the mercury pots is taken by means of a horizontal pivot on the phantom ring, but there is a connecting link underneath the rotor case which transmits any lack of balance between the mercury pots to the axis of the gyroscope. When the North end of the gyroscope axis tilts upwards the flow of mercury to the South pots creates a downwards force on the South end of the gyroscope axis, thus having a similar effect to a top heavy weight. In order that the precession causes shall make the gyroscope North-seeking, the rotor turns in an anti-clockwise direction when viewed from the South.

Damping in tilt is employed in the Sperry compass and is achieved by offsetting the gravity control link at the base of the rotor case a little to the Eastwards of centre. Thus when the North end of the gyroscope axis tilts upwards the flow of mercury to the South pots causes not only a torque about a horizontal axis, but also a smaller torque about the vertical axis. The torque about the horizontal axis causes precession in azimuth and the torque about the vertical axis causes a precession which decreases the tilt. A similar effect occurs if the North end of the gyroscope axis is displaced to the West of the meridian so that it tilts downwards.

The settling position of a Sperry compass in the Northern hemisphere must be with the North end of the axis tilted slightly above the horizontal so that the resultant excess of mercury in the South pots causes a precession towards the Westwards which exactly balances the natural drift towards the East. The excess of mercury in the South pot also causes a downwards precession and to achieve a stable settling position the North end of the gyroscope axis must lie a little to the East of North so that the downwards precession

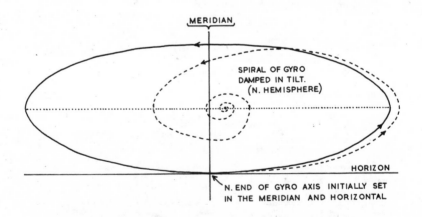

of the axis is exactly balanced by the natural upwards tilting. On the equator the gyroscope settles with its axis horizontal and in the meridian, and in the Southern hemisphere where the natural drift of the North end is Westerly the gyroscope axis settles with its North end slightly below the horizontal and to the West of the meridian. The rate of drifting and hence the tilt and the consequent displacement of the gyroscope axis from the meridian increases as the latitude increases.

**Damping error** is the name given to this displacement of the gyroscope axis from the meridian. Since it increases from zero at the equator to infinity at the poles it varies as the tangent of the latitude. It is allowed for by means of a latitude corrector mechanism which displaces the lubber line so that the compass indicates the true course.

**Course, latitude and speed error** as described on page 11 is allowed for by a corrector mechanism which can be adjusted for the ship's latitude and speed. The correction is applied to the position of the lubber line and is made to vary as the cosine of the ship's course by means of a cam which runs in a "cosine groove" cut beneath the compass card.

**Change of course, latitude and speed error.** When a vessel's course or speed is varied, the course and speed error is altered and, if no compensation were made, the gyroscope axis would tend to wander until it reached its new settling position. This is undesirable, particularly if a vessel's course or speed is altered frequently.

**Ballistic deflection** is an effect caused by the surge of mercury which accompanies a change in the North-South component of a vessel's speed. If, for instance, a vessel is heading North (so that course, latitude and speed error is Westerly) and course is altered 90°, there is a surge of mercury from the South pots to the North pots as the alteration is made. When the vessel is steadied on the new course the mercury regains its true level, but the temporary excess of mercury in the North pots as the turn is made causes a precession of the North end of the axis towards the East. This is known as ballistic deflection and it is desirable that it should be just sufficient to precess the gyroscope to its new settling position so that no subsequent wander of the compass occurs. Ballistic deflection depends upon the change in the North-South component of a vessel's speed and upon the area of free surface in the mercury pots. It is independent of the latitude and can thus be made exactly equal to the change in the course, latitude and speed error (which does vary with latitude) only for one standard latitude. The area of free surface in the mercury pots is also a factor which determines the degree of gravity control and the time taken for one complete oscillation of the gyroscope axis about the meridian. It is found that to make the ballistic deflection equal to the change in the course, latitude and speed error, the undamped period of a gyroscope should be 84 minutes.

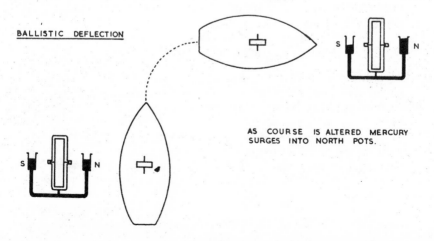

BALLISTIC DEFLECTION

AS COURSE IS ALTERED MERCURY SURGES INTO NORTH POTS.

**Ballistic tilt** is also caused by the surge of mercury which accompanies a change in North-South speed. In the case discussed above, the temporary excess of mercury in the North pots due to a 90° alteration of course from North would cause a torque round the vertical axis. Since the control link at the base of the rotor case is offset to the Eastwards, the torque would be in a clockwise direction when viewed from above and this would cause a slight upwards precession of the North end of the gyroscope axis. Thus although after an alteration of course the gyroscope has precessed horizontally to its new settling position, it is a little out of position in tilt and a slight wander will occur. No compensation is provided for this effect since it is small enough to be neglected.

**Rolling error.** If a ring is used as the bob of a pendulum, when it is made to oscillate, it tends to turn so that its maximum moment of inertia lies in the plane of the swing. The moment of inertia of a ring is greater about an axis than about a diameter so that when a vessel is rolling and the gyroscope is swinging as a pendulum in its gimbals there will in general be a torque about the vertical axis tending to turn the plane of the "vertical ring" into the plane of the swing. Such a torque would cause precession in tilt and a subsequent wander of the compass but this is prevented in the Sperry compass by attaching "compensator weights" on each side of the "vertical ring" so that its moment of inertia is the same about any axis.

**Intercardinal rolling error** is due to a combination of two effects. When a vessel on an East-West course rolls, the gyroscope swings in its gimbals in a North-South plane, thus causing mercury to surge to and fro between the North and South mercury pots although the inertia of the gyroscope rotor maintains the rotor case and mercury pots in a stable direction with reference to the horizontal. Since the surge of mercury is equal but opposite when the compass swings to the North and to the South the horizontal precession caused is also equal and opposite on each successive swing and there is no build up of an error.

When a vessel on a North-South course rolls, the gyroscope swings in its gimbals in an East-West plane and there is no displacement of mercury in the pots. The swinging of the rotor case means however that the link from the mercury ballistic to the rotor case is carried alternately to port and starboard of its normal position a little to the Eastward of bottom centre. The damping torque is thus alternately greater or less than the correct value as the vessel rolls to starboard and to port, but the average value is not affected and the settling position of the gyroscope is not disturbed.

Consider now a vessel heading in a North-Easterly direction and rolling. As the vessel rolls assume the gyro swings first in a North-Westerly direction, causing mercury to surge into the North pots and at the same time causing the link under the rotor case to be carried to the Westward of its normal position, — a combination of effects which causes an anticlockwise torque around the vertical axis of the gyroscope and hence a downwards precession of the North end of the axis. As the vessel's rolling continues the gyroscope swings in a South-Easterly direction causing mercury to surge into the South pots and at the same time causing the link to be carried to the Eastward of its normal position, — a combination of effects which also causes an anti-clockwise torque around the vertical axis of the gyroscope and again a downwards precession of the North end of the gyroscope axis. The effect of intercardinal rolling error is thus cumulative and causes a precession in tilt which gives rise to a subsequent wander of the compass.

INTERCARDINAL ROLLING ERROR ON N.E. CO.

WHEN GYRO SWINGS TO PORT                    WHEN GYRO SWINGS TO ST'B'D.

The error is approximately corrected by restricting the bore of the tubes connecting the mercury bottles so that the surge of mercury lags about a quarter of a period behind the roll. The maximum displacement of the rotor case link does not then coincide with the maximum displacement of mercury and the error is almost eliminated. Any residual error is corrected by weights on the top of the mercury pots set to give the compass a slight top heavy weight or bottom heavy weight effect so that a force is produced which compensates for the mercury flow lagging by other than exactly a quarter of a period of roll.

**Follow up system.** In order that the phantom ring can be made to follow a movement of the "vertical ring" a device is necessary which can sense a displacement between the two rings and send a signal to a motor which will cause the phantom ring to move in the required direction to "keep step" with the "vertical ring". For this purpose the Sperry compass has a transformer with an E-shaped core fitted horizontally to the phantom ring, an alternating current being supplied to the primary coil on the centre prong of the E and a secondary coil being wound on each of the outside prongs. The windings are made so that the primary induces a voltage which is equal in value but opposite in phase in each of the secondary coils. The secondary coils are connected in series, and the resultant voltage in the secondary circuit is thus zero. A piece of soft iron (the armature) is attached to the "vertical ring" so that it lies close to and across the prongs of the E. The soft iron also acts as a core to the transformer and thus increases the primary-secondary induction but,

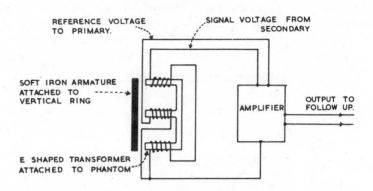

when in a central position it does not disturb the balance between the two secondaries. If however a displacement occurs between the phantom and the "vertical ring" the armature is offset to one side of the E; the secondary coil on that side then has the predominant effect and a resultant voltage is induced in the secondary circuit. The direction in which the iron armature is displaced with respect to the transformer determines the phase of the voltage induced in the secondary circuit with respect to the voltage in the primary circuit, and this is made to operate an electronic switching and amplifying device which controls the azimuth motor.

**The azimuth motor** (or follow up motor) is secured to the spider element and, by means of a pinion, it drives a large toothed wheel attached to the phantom element beneath the compass card. The direction in which the phantom element is driven is of course such that the transformer on the phantom ring is realigned with the armature on the "vertical ring".

**The transmitter.** In order that the master compass readings can be relayed to steering and bearing repeaters at convenient positions in the ship, a step by step transmitter is provided. This is attached to the lubber ring, the whole of which moves when the mechanical corrections are applied to the lubber line. These corrections are then automatically relayed to the repeaters. The transmitter consists of twelve copper segments arranged around the circumference of a circle. A rotating contactor is driven through gearing from the toothed wheel beneath the compass card. Contact is made with opposing pairs of the segments and, as the contactor moves from one pair of segments to the next, a signal is transmitted which causes a comparable movement of a step by step electric motor in each of the repeaters.

**The Sperry Minor compass** is a smaller, simplified version of the compass described above, but the basic principles of its design are similar.

## THE BROWN GYRO COMPASS

The Brown compass consists basically of a 2 Kg. rotor spinning at a rate of 14,000 revs. per minute, the rotor and its case forming a three phase induction motor. The rotor case is supported in a vertical ring by transverse bearings which allow the rotor case to move in tilt. So that the rotor case and the "vertical ring" can move freely together about a vertical axis the weight of the "vertical ring" is supported by the pressure of a pulsating column of oil maintained in the lower bearing by a small pump. An upper guide bearing is provided, but this takes no weight, and the result is that the vertical ring is free to move virtually without friction. In the Brown compass there is no need for a phantom element such as that which prevents the wire suspension of a Sperry compass from twisting and the compass card is attached directly to the top of the vertical ring.

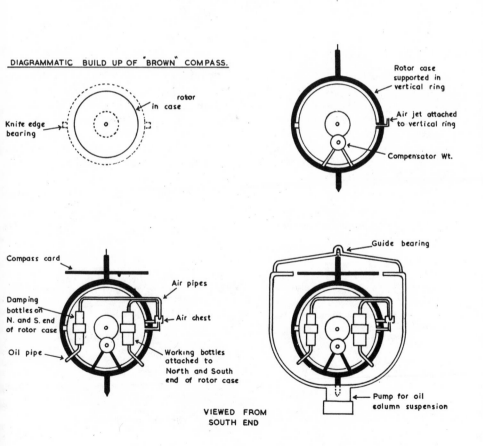

DIAGRAMMATIC BUILD UP OF "BROWN" COMPASS.

rotor in case

Knife edge bearing

Rotor case supported in vertical ring

Air jet attached to vertical ring

Compensator Wt.

Compass card

Damping bottles on N. and S. end of rotor case

Oil pipe

Air pipes

Air chest

Working bottles attached to North and South end of rotor case

VIEWED FROM SOUTH END

Guide bearing

Pump for oil column suspension

**Gravity control** is provided by two bottles of oil, one attached to each end of the rotor case. The bottles are interconnected at the bases by an oil pipe and the level of oil is controlled by a difference in air pressure supplied by air pipes connected to the tops of the bottles. The air pressure used to actuate the control is that which is built up in the rotor case by the centrifugal effect of the air which rotates with the rotor. Air enters the wheel casing around the rotor housing of the case, in this way helping to cool the Electrical Stator. The air is led from the case through the knife edges, on the East side a scoop being provided to improve the air flow. (Air through the West knife edges was used in early compasses to supply a horizontal nozzle which operated an airvane follow-up system). From the East scoop, the air is exhausted through a vertical jet into a small chest attached to the rotor case.

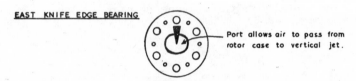

EAST KNIFE EDGE BEARING

Port allows air to pass from rotor case to vertical jet.

The chest is divided centrally by a vee-shaped block so that the air from the jet is divided equally into each half of the chest when the rotor case is horizontal, but so that any movement of the chest relative to the jet due to a tilt of the rotor case causes an excess pressure in the high end of the air chest. By means of cross over air pipes, the excess air pressure in the high side of the chest is transmitted to the oil bottle on the low end of the rotor case. The excess of air pressure forces oil to the high side bottle and thus causes a downwards force on the high end of the rotor axis. This is a bottom heavy weight effect and the Brown gyroscope has to spin in a clockwise direction when viewed from the South so that the resultant precession causes its axis to seek the meridian.

GRAVITY CONTROL OF BROWN COMPASS

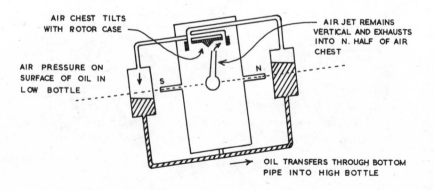

AIR CHEST TILTS WITH ROTOR CASE

AIR JET REMAINS VERTICAL AND EXHAUSTS INTO N. HALF OF AIR CHEST

AIR PRESSURE ON SURFACE OF OIL IN LOW BOTTLE

OIL TRANSFERS THROUGH BOTTOM PIPE INTO HIGH BOTTLE

**Damping** is achieved in a Brown compass by limiting the movement of the gyroscope axis in azimuth. This is effected by fitting an additional oil bottle to each end of the rotor casing. These damping bottles are interconnected by an oil pipe and are directly connected by air pipes (without a cross-over) to the air chest so that they act in opposition to the main working bottles. The flow of oil between the damping bottles is however restricted by a needle valve so that there is a time lag between a tilting of the gyroscope axis and the corresponding unbalance of oil in the damping bottles. The effect of the time lag is that the precession caused by the damping bottles does not act early enough to cause much reduction in the initial meridian seeking precession caused by the working bottles. The effect of the damping bottles does however become apparent later and, acting in opposition to the working bottles, limits the amount by which the axis overshoots the meridian. The damping bottles are made smaller in size than the working bottles so that the percentage damping is 66.2/3% which is the same as that in the Sperry compass. The angle by which the axis overshoots the meridian is reduced by a factor of two thirds on each successive transit and the gyroscope spirals in towards a settling position with its axis lying in the meridian as illustrated (Page 11) for a compass in the Northern hemisphere.

**Latitude correction.** In the Northern hemisphere a gyroscope tends to settle with the North end of its axis above the horizon so that the gravity control causes a Westward precession which exactly balances the natural Eastward drift. In the Southern hemisphere, where the natural drift is Westward, the North end of the gyroscope axis settles with a downwards tilt. With a Brown gyroscope no error is caused by this tilting but it is undesirable for mechanical reasons. In the Northern hemisphere the axis may be made to settle in a horizontal position by giving heaviness to the North end of the axis so that a Westerly precession equal to the Easterly drift is caused when the gyroscope axis is horizontal. On the equator, no such heaviness is needed and in the Southern hemisphere the South end of the axis must be made heavy. The correction is made by means of a small compensator weight pivoted to move round a scale graduated in latitude. So as to create the required North or South heaviness, the weight is attached to the rotor case (i.e. part of the sensitive element) and should not be adjusted whilst the gyroscope is running. On long voyages, the latitude compensator weight should be set for the middle latitude.

**The sensitive element** in a Brown gyro-compass consists of the rotor and its case, the working and damping bottles and the "vertical ring" and its attachments.

**Course, latitude and speed error** is not corrected mechanically in the Brown compass. Its value may be found from tables and it may then be allowed for when courses are set.

**Ballistic deflection** is an effect caused by the transference of oil accompanying changes in the North-South component of a vessel's speed. If for instance a vessel is heading North so that course, latitude and speed error is Westerly and course is altered 90° the compass swings as a pendulum towards the North. The inertia of the gyroscope causes its axis and the rotor case to remain horizontal but the vertical ring swings out of the true vertical and the air jet, attached to the vertical ring, is displaced so that pressure is increased in the

North working bottle. The resultant excess of oil in the South bottle is to some extent re
duced by a tendency for oil to surge into the North bottle. When the vessel is steadied o
the new course the oil regains its true level, but the temporary excess of oil in the Sout
bottle while the turn is being made causes a precession towards the new settling position o
the gyroscope. As with the Sperry compass, this ballistic deflection can be made equal t
the change in the latitude, course and speed error for one standard latitude only and th
dimensions of the components which provide this equality are such that the gyroscope ha
an undamped period of 84 minutes

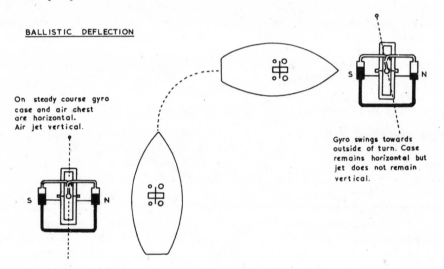

BALLISTIC DEFLECTION

On steady course gyro
case and air chest
are horizontal.
Air jet vertical.

Gyro swings towards
outside of turn. Case
remains horizontal but
jet does not remain
vertical.

**Rolling error.** If an unsymmetrical pendulum is made to oscillate, it tends to turn so tha
its greatest moment of inertia lies in the plane of the swing. In a gyroscope, swinging i
its gimbals, any such tendency would cause precession in tilt and a subsequent wander.
is avoided by fitting quadrantal compensator weights on the "vertical ring" so as t
equalize the moment of inertia of the sensitive element in all directions about the vertic
axis.

**Intercardinal rolling error** is a combination of two effects. When a vessel on an East-We
course rolls, the gyroscope swings in its gimbals in a North-South plane. Since the gyr
scope axis remains horizontal while the "vertical ring" swings out of the vertical, the a
jet is displaced with reference to the air chest and oil is transferred between the workir
bottles. This tendency is somewhat reduced by the natural surge of oil from one bottle t
the other which acts in the opposite sense as the gyroscope swings. The displacement o
the air jet is equal and opposite when the compass swings to the North and the South an
the resultant effect on the compass is zero. Owing to the time lag in the operation of th
damping bottles, the level of oil in these is not appreciably altered by a vessel's rolling.

When a vessel on a North-South course rolls, the gyroscope swings East-West in its gimbals and the torque exerted by the gravity control does not remain in a vertical plane. The orizontal component which this torque acquires when rolling to the Westward is equal to alue but opposite in name to that when rolling to a similar angle to the Eastward and the esultant precession is zero.

When the compass is swinging in an intercardinal plane, both the above effects occur. 'or example if a compass swings towards the North-West the air jet is displaced so that oil s transferred from the North to the South bottle thus creating a South heaviness which auses the North end of the axis to precess to the Eastward. At the same time, owing to he swing of the gyroscope from the vertical, the torque caused by the excess of oil in the outh bottle has a component in the horizontal plane. This acts in a clockwise sense when iewed from above and causes the North end of the gyroscope axis to precess downwards n tilt.

On the return swing towards the South-East, the air jet is displaced so that oil is transerred from the South to the North working bottle, thus creating a North heaviness which auses the North end of the gyroscope axis to precess to the Westward. This effect is equal n value but opposite in name to the precession in azimuth caused when the vessel rolls to similar angle to port and the net effect is zero. At the same time, owing to the swing of he gyroscope from the vertical, the torque caused by the excess of oil in the North bottle as a component in the horizontal plane. This acts in a clockwise sense when viewed from bove and causes the North end of the gyroscope axis to precess downwards in tilt. The recession in tilt thus acts in the same sense on each swing and its effect would be cumuitive and would cause a wander of the compass if it were not allowed for in the design of he compass.

In practice the bore of the oil pipes and the viscosity of the oil are chosen so that the ransfer of oil between the working bottles lags behind the displacement of the air jet by bout a quarter of the period of roll so that the maximum North or South heaviness aused by the transference of oil as the vessel volls occurs when the gyroscope is in the rue vertical and the resultant torque then has no horizontal component. Intercardinal olling error is thus eliminated.

The Brown "B" type compass is used as a steering compass and since no repeaters are rovided there is no need for a follow up or transmission system. (As a point of comparison t may be noted that even if no repeaters are provided for a Sperry compass it is still necesary for a follow up system to drive the phantom element so that the wire suspension is ept free of torsion.) An optical system of magnification is used for the Brown "B" type ompass.

The Brown "A" type compass is provided with a follow up system for driving a number of repeaters. The U-shaped primary of a transformer is attached to the vertical ring nd an alternating voltage is supplied to the two arms of the U on which the windings have een made in opposite senses. A secondary coil, or inductor head, is mounted on a horizontal follow up ring so that when the secondary is in the neutral position with respect to the U there is no voltage induced. If there is a displacement one way or the other, a signal voltage is induced, the phase of which depends upon the direction of displacement. This signal is amplified and made to operate a switching device so that a follow up motor drives the follow up ring and hence the secondary coil back to the neutral position with respect to the primary. The repeaters are driven so that they keep in step with the movements of the follow up ring and thus give the same reading as the compass card

## THE ARMA-BROWN GYRO COMPASS

The Brown Compass described in the previous section is in service on many ships, but new compasses of this design are no longer made. It has been superseded by the Arma Brown compass which is described below.

**Construction.** The rotor consists of a double ended 0.2 Kg. wheel which spins at 11,800 revolutions per minute. The wheel is sealed into a nearly spherical unit or ball by soldering hemispherical end shells on to the case in the form of a yo-yo. The ball is helium filled to reduce friction, to provide a conducting medium for heat dispersal and to prevent internal corrosion. Opposite the ends of the rotor axis and on the inside of each hemisphere is fitted an electro magnet. These form part of the follow up system.

Around the vertical groove of the yo-yo assembly, but without touching it, is fitted the floating gimbal. This is connected to the ball by thin horizontal torsion wires so that the ball has freedom to tilt. The gimbal is connected to the top and bottom of the containing tank by thin vertical torsion wires so that the ball and the floating gimbal together have freedom to move in azimuth within the tank. Fine helical wires are fitted around each torsion wire and these, together with the torsion wires, are used to supply electrical power to the ball.

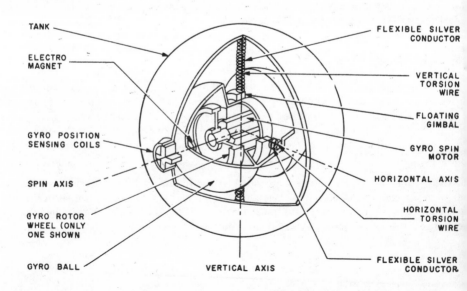

To relieve the wires of any weight, the tank containing the ball is filled with "Fluorolube". In the "hot" compass, at ambient temperature this is a solid substance and so prevents shock to the sensitive element during transportation. When the compass is in use the "Fluorolube" is heated to a working temperature of 85°C, when it becomes a liquid having S.G.1.914. The ball is constructed so that it also has S.G.1.914 and so floats in a state of neutral buoyancy. The centre of gravity and the centre of buoyancy of the ball are made to coincide.

In the "cold" compass, the fluorolube is liquid at ambient temperatures and does not require heating. The elimination of thermostats etc. increases reliability.

Unwanted twisting of the torsion wires is prevented by means of Tilt and Azimuth follow up systems which keep the tank in alignment with the ball. Two figure of eight shaped coils, mutually at right angles are fitted to each end of the tank opposite the electromagnets inside the hemispheres of the ball. When there is a misalignment in tilt or azimuth between the ball and the tank a current is induced in either the vertical or horizontal coils respectively, the phase of the current depending upon the direction of displacement. This signal is amplified and fed to a tilt or azimuth servo motor which drives gearing attached to the outside of the tank in such a way that the tank is re-aligned with the ball.

The tank and accessories are slung in gimbal rings to allow for the rolling and pitching of the ship.

**Control.** The normal functioning of the follow up system prevents any unwanted twist developing in the vertical or horizontal torsion wires, but signals may be injected into either the azimuth or tilt servo motor systems so that the tank is deliberately misaligned with the gyro ball. Such a misalignment causes a twist in the vertical or horizontal torsion wires respectively and so exerts a torque which precesses the gyro ball in tilt or azimuth. Such signals may be injected manually when the gyroscope is started so that it can be precessed approximately to its settling position.

A pendulum, moving in silicone so that it takes 1½ minutes to move through a complete oscillation, is attached to the tank. The pendulum senses any tilting of the tank and originates a signal which is injected into the tilt servo motor system. When for instance the North end of the tank lies to the East of the meridian and tilts upwards due to the rotation of the Earth, the tank is moved so as to cause a clockwise twist in the horizontal torsion wires when viewed from the East. The gyro wheel spins in a clockwise direction when viewed from the South and the resultant precession is therefore towards the meridian. In a similar way, if the North end of the tank is displaced towards the West, the downwards tilt is sensed by the pendulum and a signal is again injected into the tilt servo system causing a precession towards the meridian. The gyroscope is thus made North seeking.

**Damping** of the gyroscope is achieved by injecting a signal (also controlled by the pendu lum) into the azimuth servo motor system so that a twist is introduced in the vertica torsion wires. The twist is in such a sense that the precession of the gyro ball decreases th tilting effect of the Earth's rotation. Damping in tilt is thus provided for the Arma-Brown compass, the percentage damping being varied from 77% when it is required to settle th gyroscope quickly to 57% for normal running.

**Latitude correction.** Except at the equator, a gyroscope set North-South and horizonta tends to drift. In order that the Arma-Brown gyroscope will settle with its axis horizontal a signal is injected into the tilt servo motor system producing a precession in azimut equal but opposite to the drift rate. The strength of the injected signal is determined by control knob which can be set to any required latitude.

**Course, latitude and speed error.** The tilting of a gyroscope axis in an East-West plane i used to make the gyroscope North seeking. The upwards or downwards tilting of th North end of the gyroscope axis due to the North or South component of a vessel's spee causes course, latitude and speed error. In the Arma-Brown compass this error is elimi nated by injecting a signal into the azimuth servo motor system so that a twist is produce in the vertical torsion wires. The resultant precession of the gyro ball in tilt is equal an opposite to the rate of tilting due to the North-South component of the vessel's speed an the tilting sensed by the pendulum is that due to the Earth's rotation only. The strengt of the signal to the azimuth servo motor is determined by setting a speed control and by an input from the transmitter which varies the signal as the cosine of the ship's course.

This method of eliminating course, latitude and speed error ensures that the settling position of the gyroscope axis is in the meridian whatever the ship's course and there is n change of course, latitude and speed error when course or speed is altered.

**Ballistic deflection.** Since the compass settles in the meridian on all headings, there is n tendency for it to wander whilst seeking a new settling position after an alteration o northerly speed, i.e. there is no change of course, latitude and speed error. Ballistic de flection caused by the deflection of the pendulum does not have to be equated with change of course, latitude and speed error as with the other compasses discussed but, in stead, its effect is made very small. This is achieved by means of saturation technique which suppress large signals from the pendulum unit and by giving the compass the longe period of 120 minutes.

**Rolling error.** Since the control and damping of the gyroscope are by electrical signals an torsion wires, no gravitational controls need be attached to the gyroscope itself. Thi arrangement prevents intercardinal error.

A further source of rolling error would develop if the sensitive element had unequa moments of inertia about the North-South and the East-West axes. This is avoided by th spherical shape of the gyro ball.

**Transmission to repeaters** is achieved by causing the azimuth motor to drive a step by step transmitter which keeps the repeaters in step with movements of the gyro tank an hence with the movements of the gyro ball itself.

**Directional gyroscope.** The Arma-Brown compass may be used to indicate directions other than the meridian by eliminating the signal from the pendulum to the tilt servo system which makes the gyro ball North seeking. A signal from the pendulum is fed to the azimuth servo system so that the gyro ball is precessed to eliminate the tilting due to the Earth's rotation.

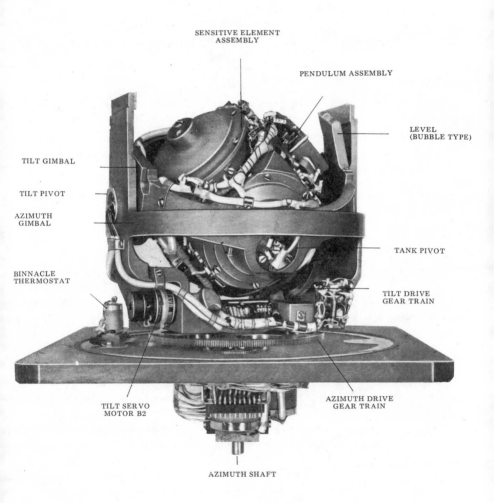

SENSITIVE ELEMENT
ASSEMBLY

PENDULUM ASSEMBLY

LEVEL
(BUBBLE TYPE)

TILT GIMBAL

TILT PIVOT

AZIMUTH
GIMBAL

TANK PIVOT

BINNACLE
THERMOSTAT

TILT DRIVE
GEAR TRAIN

TILT SERVO
MOTOR B2

AZIMUTH DRIVE
GEAR TRAIN

AZIMUTH SHAFT

# 2. The Magnetic Compass

The following definitions and formulae are basic to the study of the magnetic Compass. They are discussed more fully in "ELECTRICITY AND GENERAL MAGNETISM" a companion volume to this book.

A uniformly magnetised iron bar has a North seeking or red pole near one end and a South seeking or blue pole near the other.

Like poles repel and unlike poles attract, the force between magnetic poles being directly proportional to the strength of the poles and inversely proportional to the square of their distance apart.

A unit pole is that which is associated with a magnetic flux of one weber. The conventional symbol for pole strength (or magnetic flux) is "$\phi$".

Magnetic Moment (M) is the product of the pole strength and the length of a magnet.

$$M = 2 \, l \, \phi \text{ (Where } l = \text{half length of magnet).}$$

Unit Field Strength is that which exerts a force of one newton on a pole of strength one weber. The unit of field strength is the ampere per metre (A/m). The conventional symbol for field strength is "H", but in the following sections this symbol is often reserved for the horizontal component of the Earth's magnetic field.

The Field Strength (H) at a point distant d metres from a magnetic pole of strength $\phi$ units is given by the formula:-

$$H = \frac{\phi}{d^2} \times \frac{10^6}{16}$$

The Field Strength at a point end on to a short bar magnet and distant d metres from its centre is given approximately by the formula:-

$$H = \frac{2M}{\delta^3} \times \frac{10^6}{16}$$

The Field Strength at a point broadside on to a short bar magnet and distant d metres from its centre is given approximately by the formula:-

$$H = \frac{M}{d^3} \times \frac{10^6}{16}$$

It follows from these last formulae that the effect of a corrector magnet of constant magnetic moment in a binnacle varies inversely as the cube of its distance from the compass needles irrespective of whether the magnet is end on or broadside on to the compass.

The magnetic field strength at two positions may be compared by means of a vibrating needle. Provided the same needle is used.

$$H \propto \frac{1}{T^2} \quad \text{(where T = time of one vibration)}$$

Material that is magnetically soft will form a relatively strong temporary magnet and material that is magnetically hard will form a weaker magnet which will retain some of its magnetism permanently. Permanent magnets may thus be made by subjecting hard iron to a very strong magnetic field such as that inside a solenoid. Permanent magnets may also be made by stroking bars of hard iron with one or two permanent magnets, by mechanical vibration and by heating.

**The Earth's magnetic field.** The magnetic field due to a uniformly magnetised sphere is similar to that which would be produced by a magnet without appreciable length (known as a di-pole) situated at its centre. In a section through such a sphere, the magnetic field would appear as illustrated below.

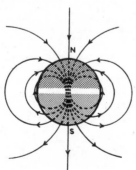

At the points marked N and S on the sphere the magnetic field is perpendicular to the surface. The comparable positions on the surface of the Earth are known as the North Magnetic Pole and the South Magnetic Pole respectively. Owing to irregularities in the structure of the Earth, these "poles" are areas rather than points. They are not situated at the goegraphical poles and are not fixed in their positions.

**Variation.** Due to irregularities in the Earth's magnetic structure, a magnetised needle, pivoted so that it can swing in a horizontal plane will not generally point true North. The direction in which it points at any position on the Earth's surface is known as the direction of the magnetic meridian. The angle between this direction and true North is the VARIATION. It is named West if the red end of the needle points to the West of true North, and East if the red end of the needle points to the East of true North.

**The magnetic meridian** at a position is the arc of a great circle whose plane contains the magnetic axis of a freely suspended needle influenced only by the Earth's magnetic field.

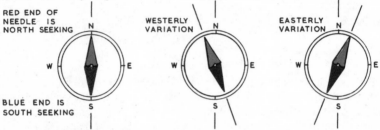

The name and the value of the Variation at any point on the Earth may be found from the appropriate Admiralty chart. On such a chart a line joining places of equal variation is known as an ISOGONIC LINE.

**Change of variation.** The change of the variation at a particular plane is not constant. The most important change is the steady one which accompanies a migration of the magnetic poles.

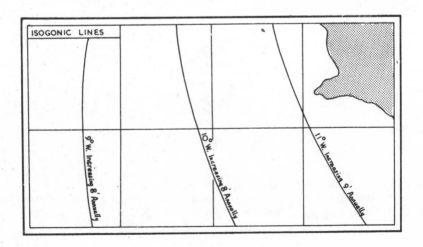

Owing to this change in the variation, isogonic lines printed on a chart are accurate for only one particular date. In order that the variation at a later date may be calculated, the annual change in variation may be printed against isogonic lines. On special charts, lines of equal change of variation may be printed. These are known as ISALLOGONIC LINES.

**The magnetic equator** only approximately follows the geographical equator. It may be defined as the line on the Earth's surface joining places where the Earth's magnetic field is horizontal. On the magnetic equator, a freely suspended magnetised needle would take up a horizontal position.

**Angle of dip.** At positions other than on the magnetic equator, a freely suspended magnetised needle will lie in the plane of the magnetic meridian but will be inclined at an angle to the horizontal. This angle is known as the Angle of Dip and is said to be positive in the Northern hemisphere where the North end of the needle is inclined downwards, and negative in the Southern hemisphere where the North end is inclined upwards.

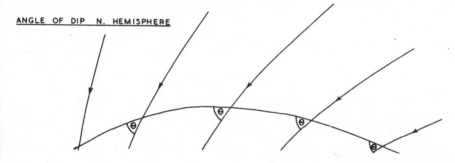

ANGLE OF DIP  N. HEMISPHERE

On a chart, a line joining places with an equal angle of dip is known as an ISOCLINIC LINE. The line of zero dip (i.e. the Magnetic Equator) is known as the ACLINIC LINE.

**Components of the Earth's field.** The direction of the Earth's total field (T) at any point lies in the plane of the magnetic meridian and is inclined to the horizontal by the angle of dip. Since a compass card is constrained substantially to the horizontal, a compass needle can respond only to the horizontal component (H) of the Earth's total field.

The diagram below shows the Earth's total field resolved into horizontal and vertical components at a position where the angle of dip is $\theta°$.

NORTHERN HEMISPHERE

ANGLE OF DIP  $\theta$

H

$\theta$

T    Z

From the diagram it is clear that:-

The horizontal component of the earth's field $H = T \cos \theta$

The vertical component of the earth's field $Z = T \sin \theta$

Also, the tangent of the angle of dip, $\tan \theta = \dfrac{Z}{H}$

H is always directed towards Magnetic North and is conventionally always considered positive.

Z is directed downwards in the Northern hemisphere and is then conventionally positive.

Z is directed upwards in the Southern hemisphere and is then conventionally negative.

SOUTHERN HEMISPHERE

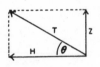

ANGLE OF DIP $\theta$

**The compass.** The simplest form of compass consists of a magnetised needle free to rotate in a horizontal plane. Such a needle tends to settle in the magnetic meridian.

PIVOTED   NEEDLE   FORMS
SIMPLE   COMPASS

This simple arrangement is unsatisfactory aboard ship. The needle would tend to oscillate and provide an unsteady compass and it would be difficult to make efficient correction on all headings for the disturbing effect of the ship's magnetic field. The mariners' compass must therefore be specially designed.

**The dry card compass** consists of a system of short magnetised needles suspended by silk threads from a light aluminium ring. Usually 6, 8 or 10 needles are employed, sym metrically disposed so that their poles lie on the circumference of a circle and the mean of the angles subtended at the centre between pairs of like poles is $60°$.

The aluminium ring is suspended from a centre piece into which is set a sapphire bearing. The bearing rests on a hard iridium point, thus forming an almost frictionless pivot. The card is maintained nearly horizontal by arranging that the centre of gravity of the card and needles is below the pivot. The weight of the card is contained largely in the aluminium ring at its circumference and it therefore possesses a large moment of inertia in comparison with its weight. This fact, in association with an appropriate magnetic moment for the system of needles, produces a stable card and no external damping is necessary. The long period of vibration achieved ensures that the card is not caused to oscillate in time with the much shorter natural vibrations of the ship.

Dry cards are usually made 254 millimetres (10 inches) in diameter, and the degree markings are then large enough to be easily read. These markings are printed on rice paper divided into segments so as to prevent any extensive error due to distortion of the paper. The period of vibration for a 254 millimetre card should be between 23-35 seconds.

## DRY CARD

FROM BELOW         IN SECTION

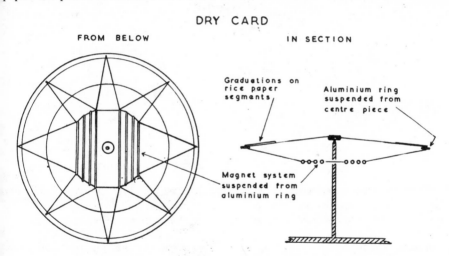

Graduations on rice paper segments

Aluminium ring suspended from centre piece

Magnet system suspended from aluminium ring

**The liquid card compass** has greater stability than the dry card compass. The effect of the liquid is to quickly damp out any oscillations which the card may tend to develop, giving the card what is sometimes termed a "dead beat" action. The liquid card is somewhat smaller than the bowl (often a 152 millimetre or 6 inch card in a 229 millimetre or 9 inch bowl) so that the card is not affected by the frictional turbulence which may develop near the sides of the bowl.

The mica or translucent plastic card is mounted on a hollow float containing the sapphire bearing. The magnetic system is enclosed and attached below the card; it may consist of separate needles or a single magnet in the form of a ring.

The liquid in the compass bowl is distilled water to which ethyl alcohol is added so that the viscosity of the mixture is lower than that of pure water and the freezing point is

−30°C. This liquid has a small coefficient of expansion, but since its volume changes slightly with change of temperature a flexible corrugated plate or an expansion chamber is fitted to the bowl.

Part of the weight of the card and magnets is supported by buoyancy and part by an iridium point fitting into the sapphire bearing. As in the dry card compass, the point of support is above the centre of gravity of the card so that the card will remain substantially horizontal in all latitudes.

LIQUID    CARD

FROM  BELOW                          IN  SECTION

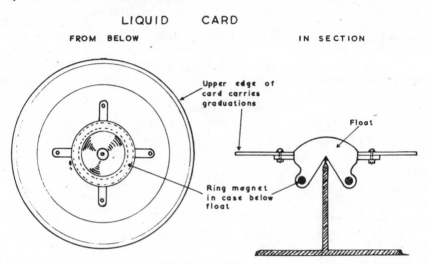

Upper edge of
card carries
graduations

Float

Ring magnet
in case below
float

**Tests for compass cards.** Both dry and liquid cards may be tested for pivot friction by deflecting the compass card a few degrees. If the pivot is in good condition the card should return to and settle in its original position with no sign of sticking or jerkiness.

**The binnacle.** A compass card is contained in a brass bowl and this is slung by means of gimbals in a binnacle. Binnacles are constructed of wood or brass, and in addition to housing the gimbals they also hold the various correctors.

**Deviation.** If a magnetic compass could be placed on a ship so that it will be acted upon only by the Earth's field the North point of the compass card would indicate the direction of the magnetic meridian and the graduation of the compass card against the lubber's line would indicate the ship's magnetic course. Local magnetic fields in a ship may cause the resultant field at the compass position to lie in a different direction from the Earth's field alone. The compass indicates the direction of this resultant field by pointing to Compass North. The angle between Compass North and Magnetic North at the Compass position is known as the Deviation. It is named Westerly if Compass North is to the West of Magnetic North and Easterly if Compass North is to the East of Magnetic North.

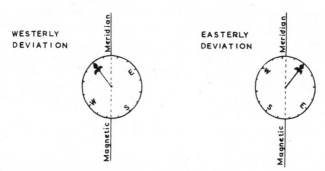

**The lubber's line.** The purpose of the mariner's compass is to indicate the direction of the ship's head and the fore and aft line of the ship is therefore indicated by a mark on the compass bowl known as the lubber's line.

**The compass course** is the angle between the compass needle and the direction of the ship's head. It defines the direction of the ship's head relative to "compass north". The compass course is indicated by the position of the lubber's line relative to the compass card.

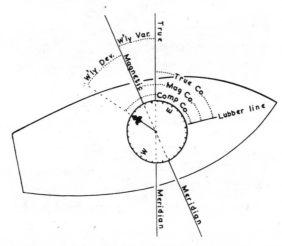

**The magnetic course** is the angle between the magnetic meridian and the direction of the ship's head. It defines the direction of the ship's head relative to "magnetic north". The difference between any magnetic course and the corresponding compass course is the deviation.

**The true course** is the angle between the true meridian and the direction of the ship's head. It defines the direction of the ship's head relative to "true north". The difference between any true course and the corresponding magnetic course is the variation.

**Ship magnetism.** A ship is built largely of mild steel and this material may be thought of magnetically as an alloy of hard iron and soft iron. It is convenient to deal with these two components separately. When a ship is built the hard iron component of its structure becomes permanently magnetised by the heating and hammering which it receives whilst subjected to the Earth's magnetic field and by the heavy welding currents which return to Earth through the ship's structure. After a ship is launched the magnetism induced in the soft iron component of a vessel's steelwork by the Earth's magnetic field will vary with the direction of the ship's head and the latitude. The magnetism in the hard iron component will be permanent and will remain constant whatever the direction of the ship's head.

The diagram below shows the magnetism induced in the soft iron component of

    a)      a ship on a Northerly heading in the Northern hemisphere.

    b)      a ship on a Northerly heading in the Southern hemisphere.

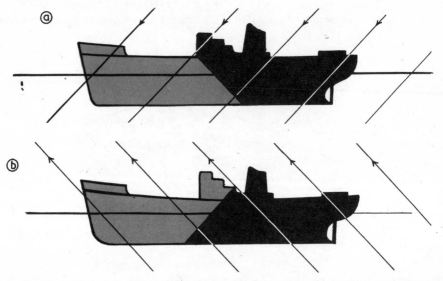

Since a ship is not a solid block of steel, the magnetism found on a ship in practice will not exactly follow the diagrams, but they are nevertheless useful as a general conception.

**Components of a ship's magnetism.** In order to analyse and correct the factors which cause deviation the hard iron and soft iron elements of a ship's magnetism can be sub-divided.

The permanent magnetic field at any compass position is resolved into three components.

Force P is the fore and aft component of a vessel's permanent magnetic field.

Force Q is the athwartships component of a vessel's permanent magnetic field.

Force R is the component of a vessel's permanent magnetic field towards or away from the keel.

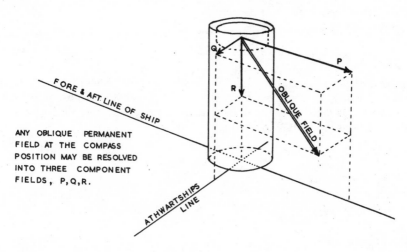

ANY OBLIQUE PERMANENT FIELD AT THE COMPASS POSITION MAY BE RESOLVED INTO THREE COMPONENT FIELDS, P,Q,R.

The soft iron effect of a ship's structure is resolved into nine component "rods", three being required to represent each of the fore and aft, athwartships and towards the keel effects. The rods are lettered in this order, systematically. Thus:-

a rod = fore and aft soft iron ⎫
b rod = athwartships soft iron ⎬ With effective poles level with the compass and
c rod = vertical soft iron.      ⎭ in the fore and aft line.

d rod = fore and aft soft iron ⎫
e rod = athwartships soft iron ⎬ With effective poles level with the compass and
f rod = vertical soft iron      ⎭ in the athwartships line.

g rod = fore and aft soft iron ⎫
h rod = athwartships soft iron ⎬ With effective poles directly beneath or above
k rod = vertical soft iron      ⎭ the compass position.

Examples of these components are illustrated overleaf.

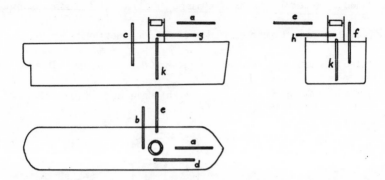

**Analysis of deviations.** If the deviation of a vessel's compass is plotted against compass headings on a graph, the result will generally be a curve without any obvious pattern, e.g. the curve below on which Easterly deviations are plotted conventionally as positive and Westerly deviations are plotted as negative.

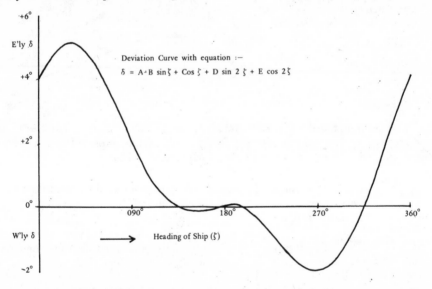

It is a mathematical principle that a continuous curve of this nature may be represented as the sum of a constant term and a number of sine and cosine curves. The process of resolving a particular curve into its component sine and cosine curves is known as Fourier analysis. It can be shown that any deviation curve resulting from the permanent and induced magnetic effects discussed above can be completely represented as the sum of not more than five component curves of particular forms. The five basic component curves whose sum would be identical to the deviation curve above are illustrated below. Thus on any chosen heading the sum of the deviations taken from the five curves below is equal to the deviation for the same heading on the curve on page 38.

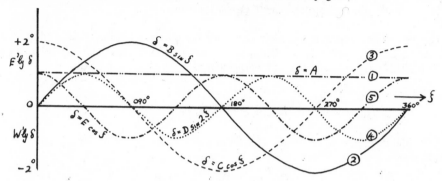

The first of these five curves is a straight line corresponding to the Easterly bias of the original deviation curve. In general, the constant deviation represented by such a line is known as COEFFICIENT A. It is conventionally positive if Easterly and negative if Westerly. The equation of this line gives the deviation ($\delta$) as:-

$$\delta = A$$

In the example above, A has the value of $+1°$.

The second curve is a pure sine curve. The amplitude of this curve, i.e. the maximum value (occurring on a heading of $090°$C) is known as COEFFICIENT B. Again it may be positive or negative. The equation giving the deviation due to this curve for any compass heading ($\zeta$) is:-

$$\delta = B \sin \zeta$$

In the example, coefficient B has the value $+2°$.

The third curve is a cosine curve. The amplitude of this curve, i.e. the maximum deviation (occurring on a heading of $000°$C) is known as COEFFICIENT C. It may be positive or negative. The equation for the component of deviation contributed by this curve is:-

$$\delta = C \cos \zeta$$

In the example, coefficient C has a value $+2°$.

The fourth curve varies as the sine of twice the compass heading. The amplitude of this curve, i.e. the maximum deviation (occurring on a heading of $045°$C) is known as COEFFICIENT D which again may be positive or negative. The corresponding equation is:-

$$\delta = D \sin \zeta$$

In the example illustrated, coefficient D has the value +1°.

The fifth curve varies as the cosine of twice the compass heading. The amplitude of this curve, i.e. the maximum deviation (occurring on a heading of 000°C) is known as COEFFICIENT E, and this also may be positive or negative. The equation is:-

$$\delta = E \cos 2\zeta$$

In the example illustrated, coefficient E has the value +1°.

The total deviation curve, being the sum of these five component curves is given by the equation:-

$$\delta = A + B \sin \zeta + C \cos \zeta + D \sin 2\zeta + E \cos 2\zeta$$

If coefficients A, B, C, D and E are known this equation gives the deviation ($\delta$) for any compass heading ($\zeta$) which may be required. The individual coefficients are now discussed in more detail.

## COEFFICIENT A

**Nature.** Coefficient A is that part of a vessel's deviation which is constant on all headings. The circular diagrams below are reminders that a positive coefficient A means Easterly deviation on all headings and that a negative A means Westerly deviation on all headings.

The **Cause** of coefficient A is a combination of an unsymmetrical pair of horizontal soft iron components. These are (i) an athwartships soft iron component with an effective pole level with the compass and in the fore and aft line (b rod) and (ii) a fore and aft soft iron component with an effective pole level with the compass and in the athwartships line (d rod). In the illustration below, induction by the horizontal component (H) of the Earth's magnetic field gives rise to a disturbing field which is always directed towards magnetic East. A constant Easterly deviation is caused on all headings and thus a positive coefficient A, the deviation curve indicating a value of +1.5°.

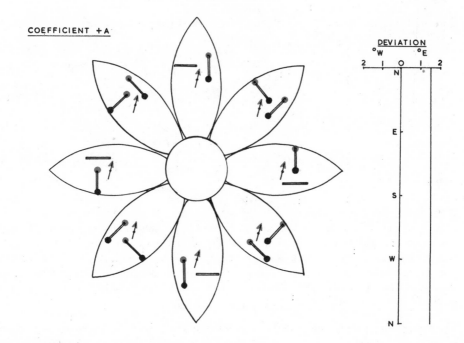

Other unsymmetrical combinations of b and d rods are possible to cause +A or −A and the following sketches are examples.

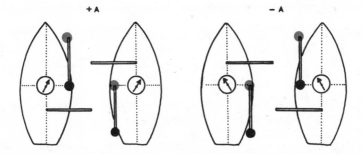

**Directive force** at the compass position may be defined as the strength of the magnetic field towards magnetic North. It should be noted, that although the magnetism induced in the b and d rods discussed above is different on every heading, the sum of the fields caused by the rods at the compass position is the same in each case and is always directed in the East-West line. There is never a component of this field towards the North or the South which would contribute to or detract from directive force.

**Change of latitude.** In a particular position, the compass needle points in the direction of the resultant magnetic field at the compass position. In the case of coefficient A this means the resultant of the horizontal component of the Earth's field (H) towards magnetic North and the disturbing field (F) towards the East or West (figure (a) below).

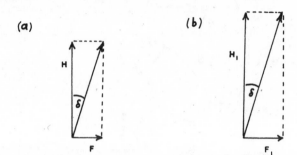

If the vessel were to proceed towards the magnetic equator, H would increase but the induction in the horizontal soft iron due to H would also increase in the same proportion (figure (b) above). The vector diagrams would be similar figures with corresponding angles equal and the deviation ($\delta$) would be unchanged. The value of coefficient A does not therefore change with change of magnetic latitude. This result may be extended to include any deviations due to induction by H in other soft iron components, these being similarly independent of magnetic latitude.

**The correction** of coefficient A is not attempted although in theory it would be possible to devise soft iron bars to act as b and d rods and so to provide the necessary compensation.

In practice the value of coefficient A is generally made negligible by careful attention to the siting of a compass on the centre line of a ship so that all steelwork is symmetrically disposed on either side.

If a compass has to be sited in a poor position coefficient A may be appreciable but this deviation is easily allowed for since it is constant in value on all headings and in all latitudes. Also, the fact that it is constant on all headings means that it does not cause an unsteady compass when a vessel is yawing in a seaway.

**Apparent coefficient A** is a constant compass error due to factors other than the magnetic effects of a ship's structure. Possible causes are if:-

1. The North-South graduations on a compass card are not parallel to the magnetic axis of the needle system.

2. The azimuth mirror used to observe deviations is out of true.

3. The wrong value of variation is used for calculating a table of deviations.

4. The lubber's line is not parallel to the fore and aft axis of the ship. Such a displacement of the lubber's line would cause an error on all headings but compass bearings would be unaffected.

## COEFFICIENT B

**Nature.** Coefficient B is that part of a vessel's deviation which varies as the sine of the compass course, thus contributing maximum deviation when heading East and West and zero deviation when heading North or South.

The value of coefficient B is the value of this maximum deviation, i.e. the amplitude of the sine curve which represents the deviation due to coefficient B on all headings.

The diagrams below are reminders that when coefficient B is positive Easterly deviation is caused on Easterly headings and Westerly deviations on Westerly headings, and that when coefficient B is negative Westerly deviation is caused on Easterly headings and Easterly deviation on Westerly headings. Deviation, which follows a pattern of this sort is said to be semi-circular.

The deviation ($\delta$) associated with coefficient B on any compass heading ($\zeta$) is given by:-

$$\delta = B \sin \zeta$$

Using the sign conventions that the sine of an angle is positive from $0° - 180°$ and negative from $180° - 360°$, and that Easterly deviation is named positive and Westerly negative, this formula specifies the correct name for the deviation on any heading as well as the correct value.

**The cause of coefficient B** is a fore and aft magnetic field at the compass position. This causes +B when directed towards the bows and −B when directed towards the stern. The field may be due to permanent or induced magnetism.

**Permanent B.** The permanent magnetism in the hard iron of a ship will, in general, cause a magnetic field at the compass position with a component (Force P) in the fore and aft line. The following illustration shows a case where a vessel has a permanent blue pole forward so that force P is towards the bows.

## COEFFICIENT + B

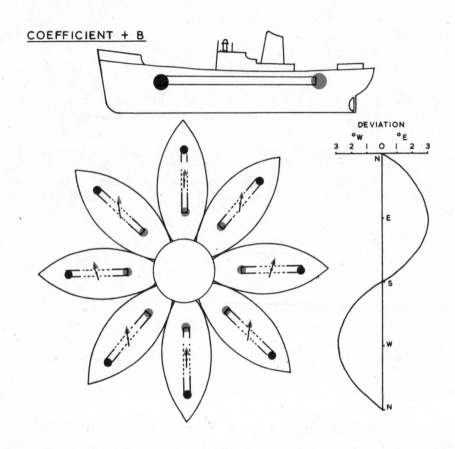

This causes Easterly deviation on Easterly courses and Westerly deviation on Westerly courses and coefficient permanent B is then named positive. On North or South, no deviation is caused, but on Northerly courses the directive force is increased, and on Southerly courses the directive force is decreased. The curve of deviation plotted against compass course is a sine curve, and the value of coefficient B is shown as +3°.

**Effect of latitude.** The parallelogram of forces when the ship's head is on East Magnetic is as illustrated overleaf (1), and the deviation, δ is caused. If the ship is on the same course in a higher latitude where the value of the Earth's horizontal field (H) is halved then, with the same disturbing force, P, the deviation is approximately doubled (2).

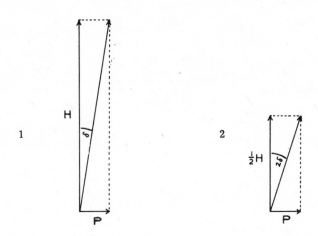

Proceeding to a lower latitude would cause H to increase and the deviation would then decrease. When small angles are involved, the deviation due to coefficient permanent B may be said to vary inversely as H. i.e:-

$$\delta \propto \frac{1}{H}$$

or, if the deviation at two places 1 and 2 are compared:-

$$\frac{\delta_2}{\delta_1} = \frac{H_1}{H_2}$$

**Correction** of coefficient permanent B is achieved by placing permanent magnets fore and aft in racks in the binnacle case, so as to counteract the fore and aft component of the ship's permanent magnetic field. In the case discussed above where the fore and aft hard iron component causes an attraction of the North end of the compass needle towards the bow, coefficient permanent B is named positive. If the attraction was towards the stern, coefficient permanent B would be named negative. To correct a +B, corrector magnets should be inserted with red ends forward. To correct a −B, corrector magnets should be inserted with red ends aft.

**Induced B** is due to induction in vertical soft iron so that an effective pole is level with the compass and in the fore and aft line through the compass (c rod). The vertical iron in a ship is generally distributed evenly fore and aft, but the siting of a compass forward of amidships means that the greater proportion of the vertical soft iron will be abaft the compass position. In the Northern hemisphere a blue pole will be induced at the top of vertical soft iron and the deviation produced will be as shown overleaf.

## INDUCED COEFFICIENT – B

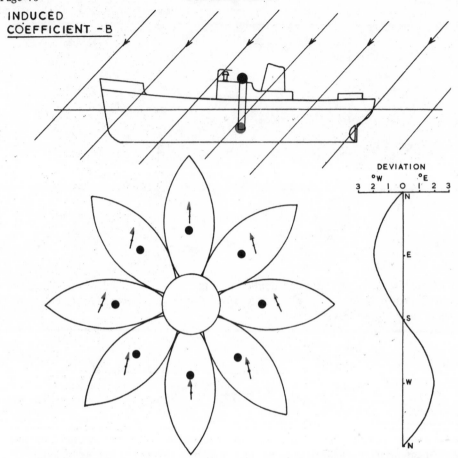

It is clear that the deviation caused depends upon the direction of the ship's head in the same way as permanent B, (i.e. it varies as the sine of the compass course) so that the above deviation curve (a sine curve) could equally well have been caused by fore and aft permanent magnetism with a red pole forward. In the above example, the c rod effect causes a negative coefficient B, the deviation curve being drawn for a value of $-2°$.

As with permanent B, the deviation due to induced B will vary inversely as H, i.e:-

$$\delta \propto \frac{1}{H}$$

In addition, the magnetism induced in the vertical iron will depend upon the value of the Earth's vertical field, Z, and this also varies with change of magnetic latitide. If the value of Z is doubled, the strength of the magnetism induced in the vertical iron is also doubled and, provided only small angles are involved the deviation will also be doubled. Thus the variation due to induced B varies directly as Z, i.e.

$$\delta \propto Z$$

When a vessel changes its magnetic latitude the value of both Z and H will alter and combining these two effects.

$$\delta \propto \frac{Z}{H}$$

or $\delta \propto \tan \theta$ (where $\theta$ = Angle of Dip).

Comparing the deviation due to induced B at two places 1 and 2:-

$$\frac{\delta_2}{\delta_1} = \frac{Z_2}{H_2} \times \frac{H_1}{Z_1}$$

or $$\frac{\delta_2}{\delta_1} = \frac{\tan \theta_2}{\tan \theta_1}$$

At a position on the magnetic equator the value of Z is zero and there is no induction in vertical soft iron. It follows that in this position there will be no deviation due to induced B. In South latitude the vertical component of the Earth's magnetic field (Z) is directed upwards and is named negative. In the Southern hemisphere the polarity induced in vertical soft iron is thus opposite to that which is induced in the Northern hemisphere. On similar courses, the deviation caused by induced B therefore will also be opposite in name in the two hemispheres.

**Correction** of coefficient induced B is achieved by securing a vertical bar of soft iron (the FLINDER'S BAR) to the binnacle so that it lies in the vertical fore and aft plane through the compass position and so that the pole induced at the top of the bar causes a horizontal field at the compass position. Where the compass is sited forward of amidships the length of Flinder's bar should clearly be attached forward of the binnacle to counteract the effect of the ship's vertical iron. Where the compass is placed aft of amidships as at the after steering position, the Flinder's bar is generally attached to the after side of the binnacle.

The Flinder's bar is contained in a brass case attached to the binnacle, the soft iron being supplied in lengths of 305 mm (12 inches), 152 mm (6 inches), 76 mm (3 inches), 38 mm (1½ inches) and two lengths of 19 mm (¾ inches). To achieve the required horizontal field at the compass position, when a length of 152 mm - 305 mm of Flinder's bar is used, the top end of the bar should be level with the compass needles. For longer lengths of bar the top should be slightly higher and for shorter lengths the top should be slightly lower than the level of the compass needles. The required level is achieved by fitting wooden spacing pieces in the lower part of the brass tude. It is assumed that the poles induced in the bar will be 1/12th of the length from the end.

**Total coefficient B** is a combination of permanent and induced components. If total B is only known in one locality these two components are inseparable and their combined effect is to cause zero deviation on North and South, and maximum deviation on East and West. On other headings the deviation caused varies as the sine of the compass course. B is named positive when Easterly deviation is caused on Easterly courses and Westerly deviation on Westerly courses. B is named negative when Easterly deviation is caused on Westerly courses and Westerly deviation on Easterly courses. The following diagrams provide a useful aid to memory.

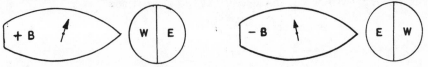

Since permanent B and induced B vary according to different rules, with change of magnetic latitude total B may be split into its component parts mathematically, provided its value is observed in two places of different magnetic latitude. See example on page 87.

**Directive force.** A magnetic field towards the bow which causes +B also causes a gain of directive force when a vessel is on Northerly headings and a loss of directive force when a vessel is on Southerly headings. A magnetic field towards the stern which causes −B also causes a loss of directive force on Northerly headings and a gain of directive force on Southerly headings. This association, between the sign of coefficient B and the comparative directive force on North and South is the key to the correction of coefficient B by deflector methods.

It should be noted that the gain of directive force on certain headings is exactly balanced by the loss of directive force on other headings so that the components which cause coefficient B have no effect of the *mean* directive force at the compass position.

## COEFFICIENT C

**Nature.** Coefficient C is that part of a vessel's deviation which varies as the cosine of the compass course, thus contributing maximum deviation when heading North or South and zero deviation when heading East or West.

The value of coefficient C is the value of the maximum deviation, i.e. the amplitude of the cosine curve which represents the deviation due to coefficient C on all headings.

The diagrams overleaf are reminders that when coefficient C is positive, Easterly deviation is caused on Northerly headings and Westerly deviation on Southerly headings and that when coefficient C is negative, Westerly deviation is caused on Northerly headings and Easterly deviation on Southerly headings. Like coefficient B, the pattern for coefficient C is semi-circular.

+ C  $\left(\dfrac{E}{W}\right)$                    − C  $\left(\dfrac{W}{E}\right)$

The deviation (δ) associated with coefficient C on any compass heading (ζ) is given by the formula:-

$$\delta = C \cos \zeta$$

Again, provided that the sign conventions are adhered to that the cosine of an angle is positive from 0° - 90° and from 270° - 360° but negative from 90° - 270°, and that Easterly deviation is named positive and Westerly negative, this formula specifies the correct name for the deviation as well as the correct value.

**The cause of coefficient C** is an athwartships magnetic field at the compass position. This causes +C when directed towards the starboard side and −C when directed towards the port side. Such a field may be due to permanent magnetism or to induced magnetism although, as explained below, the latter effect if only likely to be present at a poorly sited compass.

**Permanent C.** The permanent magnetism in the hard iron of a ship will, in general cause a magnetic field with an athwartships component (Force Q) at the compass position. In the illustration below, this component is directed towards a permanent blue pole on the starboard side causing a positive coefficient C with a value shown on the deviation curve as +2.5°.

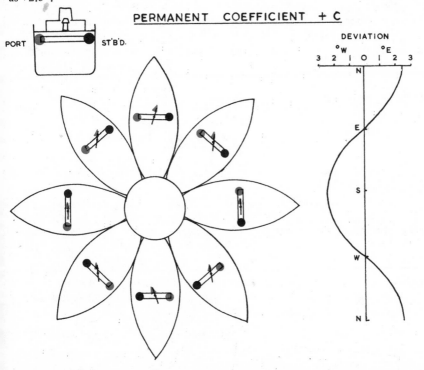

PERMANENT   COEFFICIENT   + C

**Effect of latitude.** The parallelogram of forces involved when the ship's head is on North is as shown below (1) and the deviation δ is caused. If the ship is on the same course in a higher latitude where H is half as much, provided the disturbing force (Q) remains the same, the deviation is almost doubled.

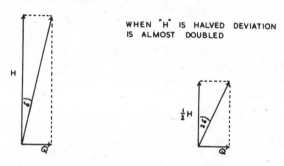

WHEN "H" IS HALVED DEVIATION
IS ALMOST DOUBLED

Proceeding to a lower latitude H will increase and with the same disturbing force the deviation will decrease. The deviation due to permanent C may thus be said to vary inversely as H in a similar way to permanent B, and comparing the deviation at two places 1 and 2:-

$$\frac{\delta_2}{\delta_1} = \frac{H_1}{H_2}$$

**Correction** of coefficient permanent C is achieved by placing permanent magnets athwartships in the binnacle case so as to counteract the athwartships component of the ship's permanent magnetism. In the case discussed above, the corrector magnets should be inserted with red ends to starboard.

CORRECTION OF COEFF. + C

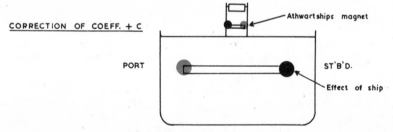

Athwartships magnet

PORT

ST'B'D.

Effect of ship

**Induced C** is due to induction in vertical soft iron so that an effective pole is level with the compass card and in the athwartships vertical plane through the compass position (f rod). If the compass is sited on the centre line of a ship, the vertical soft iron will be disposed equally to port and starboard and coefficient induced C will be nil.

If a compass is not carefully sited, coefficient induced C may be present as for example in the next illustration where a compass is offset to port of a vessel's centre line and the vessel is in the Southern hemisphere.

The red pole induced at the top of the vertical component of the ship's soft iron causes zero deviation on East and West, and maximum deviation on North or South by compass. The deviation caused varies as the cosine of the compass course and the corresponding deviation curve is a cosine curve similar to that due to athwartships hard iron with a permanent red pole to starboard. The curve illustrates a negative coefficient C with a value of $-2,5°$.

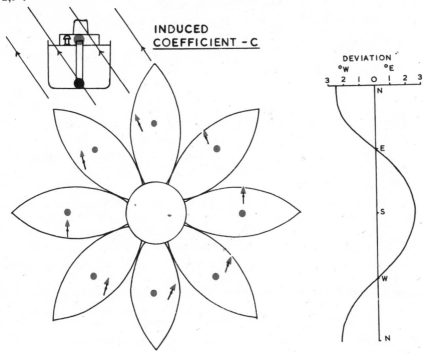

**INDUCED COEFFICIENT – C**

As with permanent C, the deviation due to induced C will vary inversely as the strength of the Earth's horizontal field (H).

$$\delta \propto \frac{1}{H}$$

In addition, the induction in the vertical soft iron f rod depends upon the strength of the vertical component of the Earth's field (Z). The value of Z is zero on the equator and increases, as the magnetic latitude increases, to a maximum at the poles. As Z increases, so the deviation due to induced C will increase and for small angles the deviation can be taken to vary directly as Z.

$$\delta \propto Z$$

When a vessel changes its magnetic latitude, the value of both Z and H will alter and, combining these two effects:-

$$\delta \propto \frac{Z}{H}$$

or $\quad \delta \propto Tan\ \theta$ (where $\theta$ = the angle of dip)

comparing the deviation due to induced C at two places, 1 and 2:-

$$\frac{\delta_2}{\delta_1} = \frac{Z_2}{H_2} \times \frac{H_1}{Z_1}$$

or $\quad \dfrac{\delta_2}{\delta_1} = \dfrac{Tan\ \theta_2}{Tan\ \theta_1}$

At a position on the magnetic equator, the value of Z is zero and there is no induction in vertical soft iron. It follows that there will be no deviation due to induced C.

In South latitudes a red pole is induced at the top of the vertical component of the ship's soft iron and the deviation caused will be opposite in name to that found on a similar course in the Northern hemisphere.

**Correction** of coefficient induced C may be achieved by securing a vertical rod of soft iron (The Flinder's bar) to the binnacle so that it lies in the athwartships vertical plane through the compass needle. When the compass is offset to port of a vessel's centre line, as illustrated, the length of Flinder's bar must be attached on the port side of the binnacle.

In a well positioned compass, coefficient induced C is negligible and a Flinder's bar is used only to correct coefficient induced B, In induced C has an appreciable value it would be possible to correct it by fitting a second Flinder's bar in the athwartships plane but in practice it is more convenient to use a single Flinder's bar slewed away from the fore and aft line so as to correct both induced B and induced C together.

In the diagram below the sides of the parallelogram represent the values of induced B and induced C. The diagonal of the parallelogram represents the resultant of the two coefficients and the Flinder's bar must be placed in this line so as to compensate for this value. From the diagram, to find the angle of slew (M) from a vessel's fore and aft line:-

$$Tan\ M = \frac{Induced\ C}{Induced\ B}$$

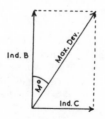

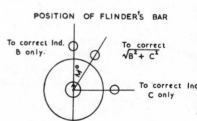

POSITION OF FLINDER'S BAR

To correct Ind. B only.

To correct $\sqrt{B^2 + C^2}$

To correct Ind. C only

To find the value of the maximum deviation caused by B and C.

$$Max.\ Dev. = \sqrt{B^2 + C^2}$$

'his maximum deviation will occur on such a heading that the diagonal of the parallelogram
ies East - West by compass.

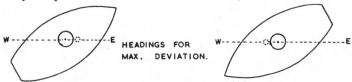

HEADINGS FOR
MAX. DEVIATION.

**Total coefficient C** is a combination of permanent and induced components. In a particular
ocality these two components are inseparable. Their combined effect is to cause zero
leviation on East and West and maximum deviation on North and South by compass.

Since permanent C and induced C vary according to different rules, with change of
atitude, total C may be split into its component parts mathematically provided its value
s observed in two places of different magnetic latitude. See example on page 99.

**Directive Force.** A magnetic field towards the starboard side which causes +C also causes
a loss of directive force on Easterly headings and a gain of directive force on Westerly
headings. A magnetic field towards the port side which causes −C also causes a gain of
directive force on Easterly headings and a loss of directive force on Westerly headings.
This association between the sign of coefficient C and the comparative directive force on
East and West is the basis of the correction of coefficient C by deflector methods.

It should be noted that the gain of directive force on certain headings is exactly balanced
by the loss of directive force on other headings so that the components which cause
coefficient C have no effect on the *mean* directive force averaged over all headings at the
compass position.

## COEFFICIENT D

**Nature.** Coefficient D is that part of a vessel's deviation which varies as the sine of twice
the compass course, thus contributing maximum deviation on the intercardinal headings
of N.E., S.E., S.W. and N.W. and zero deviation on the cardinal headings of North, East,
South and West.

The value of coefficient D is the value of the maximum deviation, i.e. the amplitude of
the sine of twice the angle curve which represents the deviation due to coefficient D
on all headings.

The diagrams overleaf are reminders that when coefficient D is positive, Easterly devia-
tion is caused on N.E.'ly and S.W.'ly courses and Westerly deviation is caused on S.E.'ly and
N.W.'ly courses; also that when coefficient D is negative, Westerly deviation is caused on
N.E.'ly and S.W.'ly courses and Easterly deviation is caused on S.E.'ly and N.W.'ly courses.
In either case the name of the deviation changes every $90°$ with change of heading and
this pattern of deviation is said to be quadrantal.

The deviation (δ) associated with coefficient D on any compass heading (ζ) is given by the formula

$$\delta = D \sin 2\zeta$$

As with previous coefficients, provided that the sign conventions are adhered to, this formula will give the name of the deviation as well as its value for any required heading.

**The cause of coefficient D** is induction by the horizontal component (H) of the Earth's magnetic field in a combination of fore and aft soft iron, with poles level with the compass and in the fore and aft line (a rod) and athwartships soft iron with poles level with the compass and in the athwartships line (e rod).

For most compass position both these components are present in the form of rods which are continuous through the compass position. The athwartships e rod effect causes +D as illustrated below and the fore and aft a rod would cause −D. In most cases the resultant coefficient D is positive because the e rod poles are closer to the compass and thus more effective than the a rod poles.

The deviation curve illustrated shows the effect of positive coefficient D with a value of +2°.

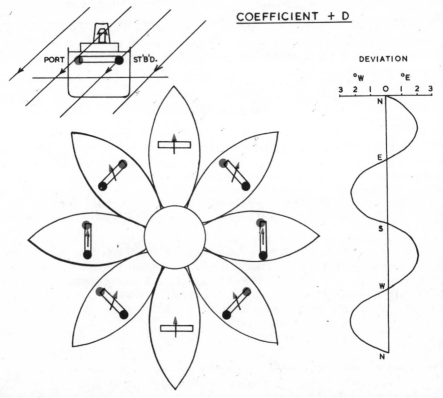

In the diagram, zero deviation is caused on headings of North, South, East and West, and maximum deviation is caused on headings of North-east, South-east, South-west and North-west by compass. The directive force is decreased on all headings except due North and South. If continuous fore and aft soft iron were also present (as in a normal ship) the effect would be to decrease all of the deviations shown above, but it would cause a further reduction in the directive force. Similar deviations to the above could be caused by fore and aft divided soft iron but the directive force would then be increased.

**Directive force.** In the usual case of a compass position with coefficient +D, the continuous rod effect is predominant causing less directive force on Easterly and Westerly headings than on Northerly and Southerly headings. In the unlikely case of a compass position with coefficient −D, the continuous a rod effect is predominant causing less directive force on Northerly and Southerly headings than on Easterly and Westerly headings. This association between the name of coefficient D and the directive force on East and West as compared to North and South froms the basis of the correction of coefficient D by deflector methods.

It should be noted that the components which cause coefficient D do affect the mean directive force at the compass position.

**Change of latitude.** The parallelogram of forces for a vessel with coefficient +D on a course of N.E. magnetic is as illustrated in figure (a) below. On the same course but in a lower latitude where H is increased the corresponding parallelogram is as in figure (b).

IN HIGH LAT.
H AND F ARE
BOTH    SMALL

a)

b)        IN LOWER LAT. H'
          AND F' BOTH
          INCREASE IN THE
          SAME PROPORTION
          AND DEVIATION
          REMAINS THE SAME

The increase in the Earth's horizontal force H, causes a proportionate increase in the induction in the ship's horizontal soft iron and thence in the disturbing force F. The 2 parallelograms (a) and (b) are similar figures with equal angles and proportional sides, and the deviation is unchanged. The deviation due to coefficient D is independent of the latitude, i.e. it is the same in both hemispheres and all latitudes.

**Correction of coefficient D** is effected by attaching soft iron spheres to the binnacle so that their centres are in the same horizontal plane as the compass needle and so that the horizontal components of induction in the spheres create an equal and opposite effect to the vessel's coefficient D.

In the usual case of a vessel with a coefficient +D due to a preponderance of athwartships continuous soft iron, the spheres should be set in place athwartships on each side of the binnacle. In this position they have the effect partly of athwartships soft iron divided about the compass position and partly of fore and aft soft iron continuous through the compass position. When the spheres are in place athwartships they cause a decrease in directive force when a vessel is on a Northerly or Southerly course and an increase when on an Easterly or Westerly course. This effect is illustrated below.

On N'ly or S'ly course
spheres athwartships
have effect of cont.
fore and aft iron.

On E'ly or W'ly course
spheres athwartships
have effect of divided
athwartships iron.

Both effects
cause coeff. −D
i.e. they correct
for + D

When the vessel is heading North or South, the effect of the spheres at the compass position is that of short magnets broadside on. When the vessel is heading East or West, the effect of the spheres at the compass position is that of short magnets end on. The increase of directive force in the latter case is thus approximately twice that of the decrease in the former case. One effect of the spheres is therefore to increase the mean of the directive force on all headings.

When coefficient +D is properly corrected the effect of the spheres is to reduce the effect of athwartships continuous soft iron and to augment the effect of fore and aft continuous soft iron until these two effects are equal. There will then be no deviation due to coefficient D on any heading.

The correction of coefficient −D is made by attaching the spheres to the binnacle in the fore and aft line, but is is unusual for a ship to have a coefficient −D before the compass is corrected.

## COEFFICIENT E

**Nature.** Coefficient E is that part of a vessel's deviation which varies as the cosine of twice the compass course, thus contributing maximum deviation on the cardinal headings of North, East, South and West and zero deviation on the intercardinal headings of N.E. S.E., S.W. and N.W.

The value of coefficient E is the value of the maximum deviation, i.e. the amplitude of the cosine of twice the angle curve which represents the deviation due to coefficient E on all headings.

The diagrams below are reminders that when coefficient E is positive Easterly deviation is caused on Northerly and Southerly headings and Westerly deviation is caused on Easterly and Westerly headings; also that when coefficient E is negative Westerly deviation is caused on Northerly and Southerly headings and Easterly deviation on Easterly and Westerly headings. Like coefficient D, this is a quadrantal pattern of deviation.

The deviation ($\delta$) contributed by coefficient E on a compass heading ($\zeta$) is given by:-

$$\delta = E \cos 2 \zeta$$

As with the other coefficients, if the sign convention is adhered to, this equation gives the name of the deviation appropriate to the particular compass heading as well as the value.

The cause of coefficient E is induction by the horizontal component (H) of the earth's magnetic field in two horizontal soft iron components which are symmetrical about a 5° line from the starboard bow to port quarter or from the port bow to starboard quarter. These components are (i) athwartships soft iron with an effective pole level with the compass and in the fore and aft line (b rod) and (ii) fore and aft soft iron with an effective pole level with the compass and in the athwartships line (d rod).

It may be noted that a combination of a b and d rod disposed *unsymmetrically* about any line through the compass would have caused coefficient A.

The diagram below illustrates a combination of b and d rods which would cause a positive coefficient E, the deviation curve being drawn for a value of +2°.

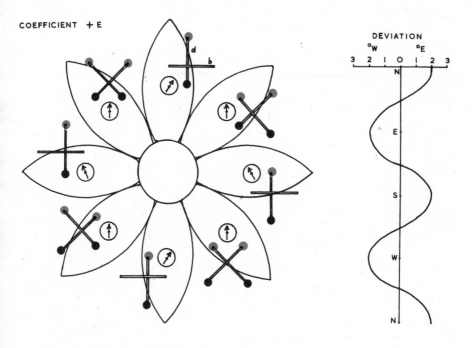

Some other combinations of b and d rods which cause +E or −E are shown below.

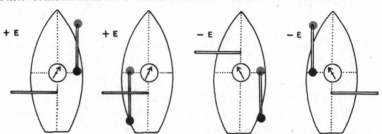

**Directive force.** The diagram illustrating a cause of coefficient +E shows that the b and d rods also effect the field towards magnetic North on intercardinal headings. Components which cause +E also cause a loss or directive force on N.E.'ly and S.W.'ly headings but a gain of directive force on S.E.'ly and N.W.'ly headings. Components which cause − E would also cause a gain of directive force on N.E.'ly and S.W.'ly headings but a loss of directive force on S.E.'ly and N.W.'ly headings.

Because the loss of directive force on some headings is exactly balanced by the gain of directive force on other headings, the components which cause either plus or minus coefficient E have no effect on the mean directive force at the compass position.

**Change of latitude.** As with coefficients A and D which are also due to induction by H in horizontal soft iron, a change of H which accompanies a change of magnetic latitude affects both the directive force and the disturbing force in the same proportion. The value of coefficient E does not change with change of H and is therefore independent of magnetic latitude.

**Correction of coefficient E.** At a well sited compass the horizontal soft iron in a ship's structure is symmetrically disposed about the fore and aft line giving rise to the a and e rods which cause coefficient D but not the b and d rods which could cause coefficients A or E. A correction for coefficient E is therefore only necessary at a poorly sited compass.

When placed in a line at 45° to a ship's fore and aft line, soft iron spheres contain athwartships components which act as b rods and fore and aft components which act as d rods. Placed level with the compass and in a line from port bow to starboard quarter they would correct +E, and placed in a line from starboard bow to port quarter they would correct −E.

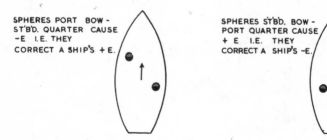

SPHERES PORT BOW -
ST'B'D. QUARTER CAUSE
−E I.E. THEY
CORRECT A SHIP'S + E.

SPHERES ST'BD. BOW -
PORT QUARTER CAUSE
+ E I.E. THEY
CORRECT A SHIP'S −E.

In practice it is possible to place a single pair of spheres between the position in which they would correct coefficient D and the position in which they would correct coefficient E so that they correct both coefficients simultaneously.

The angle of slew (M) from the athwartships (or fore and aft line) in which the spheres would correct coefficient D alone is given by:-  $\text{Tan } 2M = \dfrac{E}{D}$

(Note: Tan 2M is used instead of Tan M since the deviation being corrected is quadrantal).

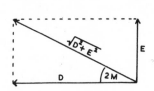
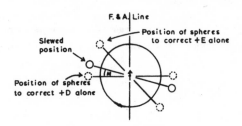

The maximum deviation due to the combined effect of coefficients D and E may be found by the formula:-

$$\text{Max Dev} = \sqrt{D^2 + E^2}$$

This maximum deviation will occur when the ship is on such a heading that the spheres (in their slewed position) will lie in the N.E. - S.W. line or in the N.W. - S.E. Line.

HEADINGS FOR MAXIMUM DEVIATION

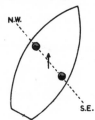
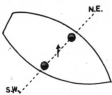

There will always be four such headings and the correction should be made on one of these.

## HEELING ERROR

**Nature.** Heeling error may be defined as the difference between a vessel's deviation when upright and when heeled on the same heading. Thus if a vessel's deviation is 2° W. when upright and 6° W. when heeled, the heeling error is 4° W. Heeling error may be caused by permanent or induced components.

**Permanent Heeling Error** is due to the component of a vessel's permanent magnetic field towards or away from the keel (Force R). This causes no deviation when a vessel is upright but, when a vessel is heeled, the field is carried out of the vertical and a deviation may be caused.

If Force R is directed towards the keel the deviation resulting when the vessel heels is towards the high side.

If Force R is directed away from the keel the deviation resulting when a vessel heels is towards the low side.

The greater the angle of heel, the further Force R is taken from the vertical and the greater the deviation caused. For small angles of heel, the value of the deviation caused can be taken to vary directly as the angle of heel.

$$\delta \propto i \text{ (where } i = \text{Angle of Heel)}$$

or comparing the deviation at angles of heel, $i_1$ and $i_2$ :-

$$\frac{\delta_2}{\delta_1} = \frac{i_2}{i_1}$$

If a vessel with a constant angle of heel is swung through 360°, and the vertical component of the ship's permanent magnetic field is directed towards the keel, the deviation caused will be illustrated below. A starboard heel is shown.

## HIGH SIDE HEELING ERROR

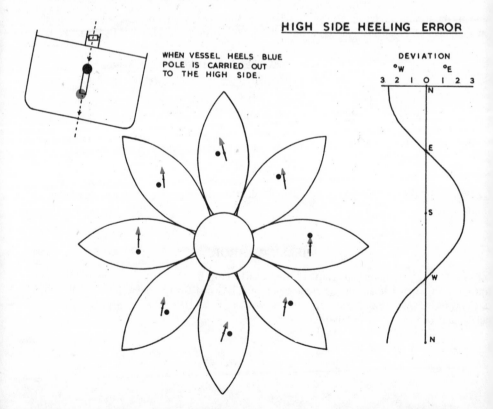

WHEN VESSEL HEELS BLUE POLE IS CARRIED OUT TO THE HIGH SIDE.

DEVIATION
°W          °E
3 2 1 0 1 2 3

The deviation is zero on East and West, and maximum on North and South by compass. The deviation curve is a cosine curve so that the deviation due to heeling error may be said to vary as the cosine of the compass course. In this respect, heeling error is similar to coefficient C which is also an athwartships effect.

**Change of latitude.** As with the deviation due to other hard iron the effect of permanent heeling error will vary inversely as H. Comparing the deviation at two places 1 and 2:-

$$\frac{\delta_2}{\delta_1} = \frac{H_1}{H_2}$$

If the angle of heel also varies the comparison between the deviations at the two places may be made in one calculation:-

$$\frac{\delta_2}{\delta_1} = \frac{H_1}{H_2} \times \frac{i_2}{i_1}.$$

**Induced Heeling Error** in a well placed compass is due mainly to two causes:-

1.  Induction in a vertical soft iron component with an effective pole beneath the compass (k rod) gives rise to a similar effect to that described above, but since the magnetism induced in the vertical iron is due mainly to the vertical component (Z) of the Earth's field, the deviation due to this cause varies directly as Z as well as inversely as H, i.e. directly as the tangent of the angle of dip.

2.  Induction by H in an athwartships component of horizontal soft iron (e rod) gives rise to coefficient D when a vessel is upright. When a vessel is heeled, this iron becomes inclined to the horizontal and acquires a vertical component in which magnetism is induced by Z. The greater the angle of heel, the greater is this induction and the greatest deviation due to this cause will occur when the angle of heel is 45°. For small angles, it can be taken that the deviation varies directly as the angle of heel.

## CAUSES OF HEELING ERROR

A PERMANENT OR INDUCED POLE VERTICALLY BELOW THE COMPASS WHEN VESSEL IS UPRIGHT BUT CARRIED TO ONE SIDE WHEN VESSEL HEELS.

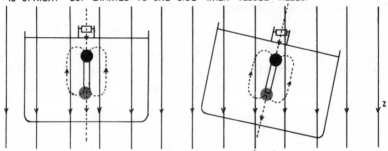

INDUCTION BY "Z" IN ATHWARTSHIPS SOFT IRON WHEN VESSEL HEELS ON N.-S. COURSES.

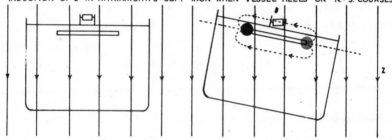

As with permanent heeling error, the deviation due to these induced effects is zero on East and West and maximum on North and South by compass. The deviation varies as the cosine of the compass course.

To summarise, it may be taken that heeling error due to a ship's permanent magnetism varies directly as the angle of heel, inversely as H and directly as the cosine of the compass course. Thus, if the permanent heeling error is known as position 1, on a specified course ($\zeta$) and with a specified angle of heel (i) the deviation at a second position on a different compass course with a different angle of heel may be calculated by the formula:-

$$\frac{\delta_2}{\delta_1} = \frac{i_2}{i_1} \times \frac{H_1}{H_2} \times \frac{\cos \zeta_2}{\cos \zeta_1}$$

where   i   =   Angle of Heel
        H   =   Earth's horizontal field
        $\zeta$   =   Compass course

The deviation due to a ship's induced heeling error varies directly as the angle of heel, directly as Z, inversely as H and directly as the cosine of the compass course. Thus if the induced heeling error is known as position (1) on a specified course and at a specified angle of heel (i) the deviation at a second position (2) on a different course and with a different angle of heel may be calculated by the formula:-

$$\frac{\delta_2}{\delta_1} = \frac{i_2}{i_1} \times \frac{Z_2}{Z_1} \times \frac{H_1}{H_2} \times \frac{\text{Cos } \zeta_2}{\text{Cos } \zeta_1}$$

where  i = Angle of Heel
Z = Earth's vertical field
H = Earth's horizontal field
$\zeta$ = Compass course

or (since $\frac{Z}{H} = \tan \theta$)

$$\frac{\delta_2}{\delta_1} = \frac{i_2}{i_1} \times \frac{\text{Tan } \theta_2}{\text{Tan } \theta_1} \times \frac{\text{Cos } \zeta_2}{\text{Cos } \zeta_1}$$

where $\theta$ = Angle of Dip

The effect of heeling error is to cause a steady deviation when a vessel has a constant angle of heel and is on a particular course. It also has the effect of causing an unsteady compass when a vessel is rolling in a seaway, because the deviation changes its name as the vessel changes her heel from port to starboard.

**Correction of heeling error.** The deviation due to heeling error is corrected by introducing permanent magnets set vertically in a holder (or bucket) beneath the compass. This arrangement introduces a vertical field at the compass position. The field may be varied by raising or lowering the bucket or by varying the number of magnets used. Whatever the number of magnets used; they should always be arranged symmetrically. Since an entirely permanent magnetic field is used to correct a combination of permanent and induced components, the correction of heeling error does not remain effective when a vessel's magnetic latitude changes.

It should be noted that heeling error due to k rod and e rod components is partly corrected by the vertical and athwartships components respectively of the soft iron spheres which are used to correct coefficient D. For this reason it is important that the spheres should be in position before the correction of heeling error is made with vertical magnets.

**Induction in a 'g' rod component,** i.e. induction by the horizontal component of the earth's magnetic field (H) in fore and aft soft iron with an effective pole beneath (or above) the compass is also a cause of heeling error. In the case illustrated the vessel has a constant starboard heel and the heeling error caused is zero on East and West but maximum and of the same name when heading North or South by compass. The deviation varies as the cosine squared of the compass course as well as directly as the angle of heel.

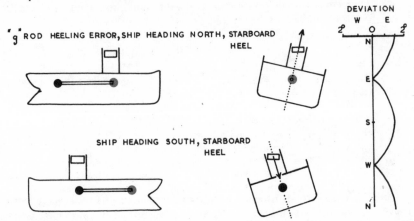

When the horizontal component (H) of the Earth's magnetic field changes, the induction in the g rod changes in the same proportion. Since the directive force and the disturbing force maintain the same proportion, g rod heeling error does not vary with changes of magnetic latitude.

Comparing the g rod heeling error on two different headings and with two different angles of heel:-

$$\frac{\delta_2}{\delta_1} = \frac{i_2}{i_1} \times \frac{\text{Cos}^2 \zeta_2}{\text{Cos}^2 \zeta_1}$$

Heeling error due to g rod induction can usually be assumed to be small and no correction is normally applied. However the correction for the previously discussed causes of heeling error is preferably made with a vessel heading East or West magnetic so that there is no magnetism induced in the fore and aft g rod to influence the vertical force instrument readings (see page 99.)

**Induction in a 'c' rod,** i.e. induction by H in vertical soft iron with a pole level with the compass and in the fore and aft line is another cause of heeling error. When a vessel is upright, the only induction in a c rod is by the vertical component (Z) of the Earth's magnetic field and this causes coefficient B as discussed on page 70. When a ship is heeled on Easterly ot Westerly course, induction by H also occurs. This latter effect increases as the angle of heel increases and therefore causes heeling error which varies directly as the angle of heel.

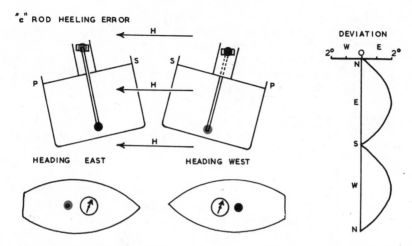

"c" ROD HEELING ERROR

HEADING EAST          HEADING WEST

DEVIATION

For a vessel with a constant angle of heel the error is zero when heading North and South but maximum and of the same name when heading East or West. It thus varies as the sine squared of the compass course and is noteworthy as the only cause of heeling error when heading East or West.

As with other effects caused by H induction (A, E and g rod heeling error) c rod heeling error is independent of magnetic latitude. Comparing the deviation due to this cause in two different situations'-

$$\frac{\delta_2}{\delta_1} = \frac{i_2}{i_1} \times \frac{Sin^2 \zeta_2}{Sin^2 \zeta_1}$$

Heeling error due to c rod induction is corrected by the Flinder's bar which is placed primarily to correct the induced part of coefficient B. Since the position of the Flinder's bar is often a matter of estimation it follows that the correction of c rod heeling error is not always satisfactory. If present it is normally small but has the effect of causing an unsteady compass on Easterly and Westerly headings.

**Lambda.** The direction which a compass needle assumes at the compass position depends partly on the directive force exerted on the needle towards magnetic North and partly on the disturbing forces present. The ratio of the mean directive force towards magnetic north at the compass position to the directive force ashore is given the symbol $\lambda$ (lambda). In order that deviations are not to be too great, it is clear that lambda should not be too small.

The effect of permanent magnetism and vertical soft iron will have an effect on directive force on a particular heading, but on opposite headings the effect will always be equal and opposite. When the mean of the directive forces on all headings is taken, the effect of permanent magnetism and vertical soft iron cancels out and $\lambda$ is therefore independent of these components.

Horizontal soft iron which is continuous through the compass position causes a mean loss of directive force and horizontal soft iron which is divided about the compass position causes an increase. Aboard the majority of ships continuous horizontal soft iron has a greater effect than divided soft iron and the mean directive force towards magnetic North aboard ship $(H_1)$ is less than that ashore (H). Lambda will thus normally be less than unity and is found from the formula:-

$$\lambda = \frac{H_1}{H}$$

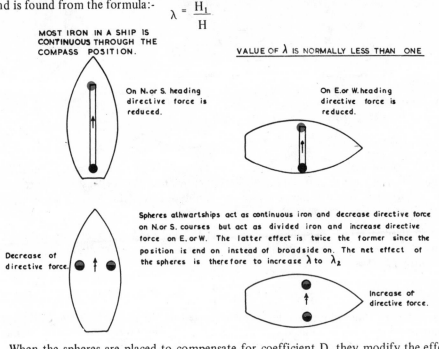

**MOST IRON IN A SHIP IS CONTINUOUS THROUGH THE COMPASS POSITION.**

On N. or S. heading directive force is reduced.

**VALUE OF $\lambda$ IS NORMALLY LESS THAN ONE**

On E. or W. heading directive force is reduced.

Decrease of directive force.

Spheres athwartships act as continuous iron and decrease directive force on N. or S. courses but act as divided iron and increase directive force on E. or W. The latter effect is twice the former since the position is end on instead of broadside on. The net effect of the spheres is therefore to increase $\lambda$ to $\lambda_2$

Increase of directive force.

When the spheres are placed to compensate for coefficient D, they modify the effect of a vessel's horizontal soft iron. When the spheres are in the North-South line they have the effect of divided soft iron and increase the directive force. When the spheres are in the East-West line from the compass position they have the effect of continuous soft iron. The former effect will be approximately twice that of the latter since the spheres in the North-South line are "end on" to the compass and in the East-West line they are "broadside" on to the compass. The net effect is to cause a desirable increase in directive force. When the spheres are in position, the ratio of the mean directive force towards magnetic North aboard to the directive force ashore is given the symbol $\lambda_2$.

**MU.** The vertical field at the compass position is the sum of the vertical component of the Earth's magnetic field (Z) plus the vertical fields due to the permanent (force R) and induced (k rod) components of a vessel's magnetism towards or away from the keel. The ratio between the mean vertical field at the compass position $(Z_1)$ and the vertical field ashore (Z) is given the symbol $\mu$ (mu). Thus:-

$$\mu = \frac{Z_1}{Z}$$

The value of mu is affected by the soft iron spheres used to correct coefficient D and also by the vertical magnets used to correct heeling error. The value of the ratio with the correctors in place is distinguished by the symbol $\mu_2$.

**Combination of coefficients.** The deviation on any particular heading of a ship is due to a combination of effects from all the coefficients. Coefficient A gives rise to a constant deviation whatever the heading. The effect of coefficient B varies as the sine of the compass course. The effect of coefficient C varies as the cosine of the compass course. The effect of coefficient D varies as the sine of twice the compass course and the effect of coefficient E varies as the cosine of twice the compass course. Thus on a heading of $\zeta$ by compass:-

$$\delta = A + B \sin \zeta + C \cos \zeta + D \sin 2\zeta + E \cos 2\zeta$$

If the vessel has an angle of heel, and heeling error is present, then this also will vary as the cosine of the compass course in a similar way to coefficient C.

If observations of the deviation were made on five random headings, five equations could be written down with the five coefficients as unknowns. Solution of the five equations would be tedious although not difficult in principle.

**Analysis.** The value of the five coefficients may more conveniently be calculated if the deviation is observed with the ship's head on eight equidistant points of the compass, including compass North. Each coefficient may then be found according to a rule as follows:-

A.    All the coefficients except A give rise to deviations on headings which can be grouped in pairs so that for each pair of headings the deviations are equal in value but opposite in name (e.g. the deviation due to B on N.E. is equal and opposite to that on S.W.). Coefficient A may thus be found by adding all the deviations and dividing the sum by eight. The other coefficients are then eliminated.

B.    • Coefficient 'B has maximum deviation of East and West by compass, but the name on West is opposite to the name on East. Coefficients A and E, which also cause deviation on East and West by compass, are of the same name on each of these courses. The value of coefficient B may thus be calculated by reversing the name of the deviation on West, adding this figure to the deviation on East, and dividing the sum by two. This process eliminates both A and E.

C.    Coefficient C may be calculated similarly by reversing the name of the deviation on South, adding the figure to the deviation on North and dividing the sum by two, a process which again eliminates A and E. It may be noted there that, if the vessel has a constant angle of heel during the swing, the coefficient found in this way includes heeling error as well as C.

D.  On the intercardinal points, coefficients A, B, C and D all contribute to the deviation. If the value of the deviation on N.E., S.E., S.W., and N.W. are noted coefficient D may be calculated by reversing the name of the deviations on S.E. and N.W., adding these figures to the deviations on N.E. and S.W. and dividing the sum by four. This process eliminates coefficients A, B and C.

E.  If the values of the deviation on N., E., S., and W. are noted, coefficient E may be calculated by reversing the name of the deviations on E. and W., adding these figures to the deviations on N. and S. and dividing the sum by four. This process eliminates coefficient A, B and C.

This method of finding the separate coefficients from an observed set of deviations is best carried out in the form of a tabulation as in the following example.

To find the value of the separate coefficients given that when the vessel is swung through 360° the deviations on eight points of the compass are as follows: on N. 2½° W., on N.E. 1¾° W., on E. 3½° E., on S.E. 8° E., on S. 5½° E., on S.W. ¼° W., on W. 2½° W., and on N.W. 2° W.

| COMPASS CO. | A | B | C | D | E |
|---|---|---|---|---|---|
| N. | $2\frac{1}{2}°$ W | | $2\frac{1}{2}°$ W | | $2\frac{1}{2}°$ W |
| N.E. | $1\frac{3}{4}°$ W | | | $1\frac{3}{4}°$ W | |
| E. | $3\frac{1}{2}°$ E | $3\frac{1}{2}°$ E | | | $3\frac{1}{2}°$ W |
| S.E. | $8°$ E | | | $8°$ W | |
| S. | $5\frac{1}{2}°$ E | | $5\frac{1}{2}°$ W | | $5\frac{1}{2}°$ E |
| S.W. | $\frac{1}{4}°$ W | | | $\frac{1}{4}°$ W | |
| W. | $2\frac{1}{2}°$ W | $2\frac{1}{2}°$ E | | | $2\frac{1}{2}°$ E |
| N.W. | $2°$ W | | | $2°$ E | |
| | 8)8° E | 2)6° E | 2)8° W | 4)8° W | 4)2° E |
| | 1° E | 3° E | 4° W | 2° W | $\frac{1}{2}°$ E |
| | A = +1 | B = +3 | C = −4 | D = −2 | E = +½ |
| | (E) | (W E) | (W / E) | (E W / W E) | ⊗ |

It should be noted that, when the mean deviation is easterly, the corresponding coefficient is positive and when the mean deviation is westerly the corresponding coefficient is negative.

It may be noted also that if the compass error is given instead of the deviation for each direction of the ship's head, the analysis may be carried out as above, but the result obtained from the first column of the table will be the combined effect of coefficient A and the Variation. If coefficient A can be taken to be negligible, this provides a method of ascertaining the Variation and it also follows that if a compass bearing of a distant fixed object is observed with the ship's head on each of eight equidistant points of the compass, the mean bearing will be the correct Magnetic bearing of the object. This is sometimes useful when a ship is swung to correct compasses (see also page 72).

## CORRECTION OF THE COMPASS

**General.** A compass needle on a ship is deviated from Magnetic North by induced or permanent magnetic fields associated with the structure of the ship. The compass is corrected by introducing permanent magnets and soft iron correctors so as to oppose these disturbing fields. Since there is an interaction between the various correctors it is important that a particular sequence should be followed when a compass is adjusted.

**Analysis method.** A theoretically correct method of adjusting a compass is to analyse the observed deviations to calculate each of the coefficients in turn, and to compensate for these by using the appropriate correctors.

Since the correctors interact (e.g. the thickness of a Flinder's bar causes coefficient D and permanent magnetism in the spheres may cause coefficients B and C) it is necessary to proceed in the order, (i) Flinder's bar, (ii) spheres, (iii) heeling error magnets, (iv) fore and aft athwartships magnets. Also the appropriate deviations must be observed for analysis at each stage of the adjustment since they will be modified as the adjustment proceeds. The analysis method is therefore a very time consuming method of adjustment and is almost never used in practice.

**Tentative method.** Various "tentative" methods of adjusting a compass are available whereby a formal analysis of deviations is not attempted but where the deviation observed on a particular heading is dealt with at that stage before swinging the ship onto the next heading in sequence. A suitable procedure is as follows:-

1.    A length of Flinder's bar is first introduced in order to correct for an estimated value of coefficient induced B. The Flinder's bar will be placed on the fore side of the binnacle if it is sited in the usual position on a bridge forward of amidships. The length of Flinder's bar used must be estimated by the compass adjuster from his experience with other ships.

2. The spheres are then set in an estimated position athwartships to correct for the ship's expected +D (Usual position is at about the middle of the brackets). If time is available the ship may then be swung so that the deviations on N.E., S.E., S.W. and N.W. can be observed. The value of the residual coefficient D may then be calculated and the spheres may be adjusted to correct for this. If a +D is calculated, the spheres in their initial position are undercompensating and must be moved inwards on their brackets. If a —D is calculated, the spheres in their initial position are overcompensating and must be moved outwards. If a large —D is calculated, one or both spheres may have to be removed and in the unusual event of the ship alone having a —D the spheres would have to be shipped in the fore and aft line.

**NOTE:-** It is necessary to place the Flinder's bar in position before the spheres because the thickness of the bar causes a +D effect. The spheres are then placed in position so that all the soft iron correction is made before the permanent magnet correctors are introduced. This is necessary because if the permanent magnets were inserted first the magnetic fields caused would be modified when the spheres and Flinder's bar were set in position. Coefficient induced C and coefficient E are negligible in a well sited compass. If they are considered to be appreciable they should be corrected by slewing the Flinder's bar and the spheres immediately after the correction of coefficient induced B and coefficient D respectively.

3 The correction of heeling error is next attended to. Since it is not convenient to heel a ship for this purpose, a vertical force instrument is employed. This instrument consists of a magnetic needed pivoted horizontally a little above its centre of gravity so that, in the absence of a magnetic field, it would lie with its axis horizontal. In the presence of a vertical magnetic field, however, the needle would be tilted. In the Northern hemisphere the North end of the needle will tilt downwards, and in the Southern hemisphere the South end will tilt downwards. The force causing the needle to tilt from the horizontal is the vertical component (Z) of the Earth's field. The effect of Z may be counteracted by sliding a weight along the needle until it remains balanced in a horizontal position. The distance of the weight from the pivot is proportional to Z and may be measured by reading the graduation on the needle against the side of the weight.

DIAGRAM OF
VERTICAL FORCE INSTRUMENT                                   Designed to fit
into binnacle

The vertical force instrument if first levelled ashore at a position free from disturbing magnetic fields and the reading (N) is then proportional to Z. The vertical force instrument is then placed in the compass position, preferably with the ship on an Easterly or Westerly heading.

If the rider weight were left against the same graduation as was noted ashore the needle would, in general, be found to lie inclined at an angle to the horizontal since the vertical field at the compass position is the resultant of Z, the vertical component of permanent magnetism (force R) and vertical induced magnetism (k rod). If vertical magnets were then introduced into the binnacle until the needle became horizontal, the vertical field at the compass position would be reduced to Z alone, with force R and the k rod effect (and their associated heeling error) eliminated.

In practice, such a correction would be incomplete because it is also necessary to make allowance for the effect of athwartships soft iron (e rod) which causes heeling error but which has no effect on the vertical field (and hence on the vertical force instrument) when a vessel is upright. This difficulty is resolved by noting that $\lambda_2$ is a measure of the effect of horizontal soft iron in a ship as modified by the spheres (see page 66). The contribution of horizontal soft iron to heeling error is allowed for by multiplying the ashore reading of the vertical force instrument by the value of $\lambda_2$. The weight is reset to this product before the instrument is placed in the compass position and the needle levelled by adjusting vertical magnets.

Because of the way in which it is used, $\lambda_2$ is known as the **Ships Multiplier,** and after correction this is the ratio of the vertical field at the compass position to the vertical field ashore. That is the proper correction of heeling error produces a value of $\mu_2$ numerically equal to $\lambda_2$.

The correction of heeling error is thus to note the scale reading (N) of the vertical force instrument when ashore. Then to set the weight at a graduation on the vertical force instrument equal to the product of the scale reading ashore and the ship's multiplier (N x $\mu_2$). With this setting, and the vertical force instrument in the compass position the needle is brought to the horizontal by means of the heeling error magnets.

4. Coefficients permanent B and permanent C are next attended to, the coefficient causing the greatest deviation being dealt with first. If coefficient B causes the greatest deviation the ship is steadied on East or West by compass, fore and aft magnets being introduced into the binnacle to eliminate the deviation found.

Coefficient permanent C is then corrected by steadying the ship on North or South by compass. Athwartships permanent magnets are then introduced into the binnacle to eliminate the deviation found.

5. Finally the ship's head is steadied on the intercardinal point between the headings used for the previous two adjustments and the deviation found is removed by altering the position of the spheres.

6. The compass should now be reasonably well corrected, but further adjustment to coefficient B may be made by steadying the ship on a course (E. or W. by compass) opposite to that on which the original correction for coefficient permanent B was made. Any deviation showing is then halved by readjusting the fore and aft magnets.

7. The ship is then steadied on a course (N. or S. by compass) opposite to that on which the original correction for coefficient permanent C was made. Any deviation showing is then halved by readjusting the athwartships permanent magnets.

The correction of a compass as above may be carried out during a single swing of the ship through 360°. It is then necessary to make a further swing so that the residual deviation on each point (or at least on eight equidistant points) of the compass may be observed. A deviation curve or table is then drawn up. It is important to realise that unless the length of Flinder's bar is correctly estimated, the correction of coefficient B will remain satisfactory only for one magnetic latitude. Heeling error which is composed of permanent and induced effects is corrected entirely with permanent magnets and this correction will also only remain satisfactory for one magnetic latitude.

**Methods of observing deviation.** In order to find the deviation of each heading of the ship during the swing it is necessary to compare a magnetic bearing with a compass bearing. This may conveniently be achieved by making a swing at a considerable distance from a conspicuous landmark. If the ship's position is known the magnetic bearing may be taken from a chart and may be compared with observed compass bearings to find the deviation on each heading of the ship. If the landmark is sufficiently distant and the vessel is swung in a circle of samll diameter, the magnetic bearing does not change appreciably during the operation.

The magnetic bearing of a distant object may also be found by taking the mean of a number of compass bearings. In theory the mean of the compass bearings on eight or sixteen compass headings might appear appropriate in the interests of accuracy but, since the ship must be steadied for some minutes on each heading before a bearing is observed. this would be a very time-consuming exercise. In practise the mean of the compass bearings on headings of East and West by compass is sufficient. Compass bearings on other headings would be affected by unsteadiness of the compass due to uncorrected heeling error and would contribute little to the accuracy of the derived magnetic bearing.

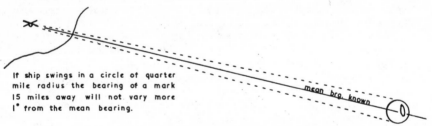

If ship swings in a circle of quarter mile radius the bearing of a mark 15 miles away will not vary more 1° from the mean bearing.

A second method of obtaining a magnetic bearing is to use a bearing compass which is set up ashore (or in a wooden boat) so that it is free from disturbing magnetic fields. When the deviation on one particular heading of the ship is required, a pre-arranged signal is made and bearings of ship and shore compass are observed simultaneously one from the other and noted. The bearings taken by the shore (or boat) compass may be taken as magnetic bearings and when reversed they may be compared with the compass bearing taken from the ship in order to obtain the deviations. Efficient communication must be maintained so that the readings of the bearing compass can be transmitted to the ship as soon as they have been observed.

Bearings of astronomical bodies may also be used to find the deviation on each heading, but a number of computations are necessary to calculate the true bearings of a body at the same times as the compass bearings are observed. This may conveniently be done beforehand to cover the period during which it is expected that the swing will be carried out.

In conditions of poor visibility, deviations may be found by comparing the ship's magnetic compass headings with the gyro compass headings. This method does not give great accuracy and is not recommended if other means of observing the deviation are available.

It is important that when a compass is corrected the factors which may effect the deviation should be in their normal seagoing state. The ship should be upright, derricks should be stowed in their seagoing position and the funnel at its seagoing temperature. No moveable iron or magnetic material should be allowed close to the compass.

## SECTION OF BINNACLE

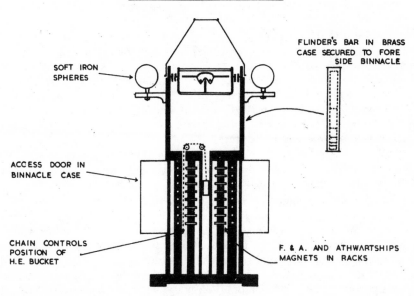

FLINDER'S BAR IN BRASS CASE SECURED TO FORE SIDE BINNACLE

SOFT IRON SPHERES

ACCESS DOOR IN BINNACLE CASE

CHAIN CONTROLS POSITION OF H.E. BUCKET

F. & A. AND ATHWARTSHIPS MAGNETS IN RACKS

**Deflector method.** If a vessel's compass has to be corrected when, as for example in conditions of poor visibility, suitable landmarks for observing compass bearings cannot be seen, a method of correcting the compass by comparing the value of the directive force on suitable headings of the ship may be used. One instrument for making such a comparison is the deflector and the type generally used in the United Kingdom is the Kelvin(Thomson) deflector.

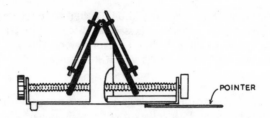

POINTER

The Kelvin deflector consists of two equal permanent magnets hinged together at two unlike poles. The poles at the hinge, being equal and opposite, cancel out and the magnetic effect of the two magnets is equivalent to that of a single magnet of constant pole strength but with a magnetic moment which can be varied by altering the distance between the free poles. The direction of the magnetic axis of the equivalent magnet is indicated by a pointer on the base of the instrument. The distance apart of the poles (and hence the magnetic moment) may be adjusted by means of a screw and is indicated against a graduated scale. The base of the instrument is non-magnetic and is constructed so that the instrument may be accurately centred over the compass bowl while free to be rotated in azimuth.

The deflector is used by steadying the ship on the heading for which the directive force is to be measured and maintaining the course by means of the steering compass. The deflector is placed in position on the standard compass bowl with the blue end of the deflector over the North point of the compass card and is then turned in azimuth and adjusted until the compass card has been deflected 90° from its original position. In order to avoid appreciable errors the magnetic axis of the deflector should lie in a direction about 80° from the North point of the compass card when the deflection has been achieved. It is important, when subsequent deflections are made on other headings, that this angle should always be the same and that the deflection should be exactly 90° so that differing directive forces are balanced only by differing adjustments and are thus indicated by corresponding readings of the deflector scale.

The correction of the compass is made by first setting the Flinder's bar and spheres in an estimated position, and then obtaining readings of the deflector while the ship's head is steadied on North and South. In general the readings on these two headings will differ because the directive force will be influenced by a fore and aft magnetic field. If the deflector reading, and hence the directive force, is greater on North than on South, this is clearly due to a magnetic field directed towards the bow. Such a magnetic field would cause no deviation on either North or South but would cause Easterly deviation on an Easterly course i.e. coefficient +B. To eliminate the magnetic field towards the bow, fore and aft magnets should be inserted in the binnacle with red ends forward until a 90° deflection of the compass card is achieved with the deflector set to a reading which is the mean of the original readings on North and South. If the original deflector reading on South had been greater than that on North, the magnets would have had to be inserted with red ends aft to correct coefficient −B.

To correct coefficient C, deflector readings are observed on courses of East and West. If the directive force on East is greater than the directive force on West, an athwartships magnetic field directed towards the port side is clearly present. Such a field would cause no deviation on either East or West but when heading North it would cause Westerly deviation, i.e. coefficient −C. To eliminate the magnetic field towards the port side, athwartships magnets should be inserted in the binnacle with red ends to port until a 90° deflection of the compass card is achieved with the deflector set to a reading which is the mean of the original readings in East and West. If the original deflector reading on West had been greater than that on East, the magnets would have had to be inserted with red ends to starboard to correct coefficient +C.

To correct coefficient D the mean deflector reading on North and South is compared with the mean deflector reading on East and West. If the mean directive force on North and South is greater than the mean on East and West, the cause could be either fore and aft horizontal soft iron divided about the compass position or athwartships horizontal soft iron continuous through the compass postion. No deviation would be caused on North, South, East or West but either of these effects (or a combination of the two) would cause Easterly deviation on a North-easterly course, i.e. coefficient +D. To reduce the directive force on North and South and increase it on East and West the soft iron spheres (already in place athwartships) should be moved closer until a 90° deflection of the compass card is achieved with the deflector set to a reading which is the mean of the mean reading on North and South, and the mean reading on East and West. If the mean reading on East and West had been greater than the mean reading on North and South the cause could have been fore and aft horizontal soft iron continuous through the compass position or athwartships horizontal soft iron divided about the compass position. Either of these distributions would cause coefficient −D and the spheres would then have had to have been moved outwards on their brackets.

The deflector method of correcting a compass does not give such accurate results as the tentative method and should only be used when conditions make it necessary.

**Gaussin error.** When a vessel is altering heading to port or to starboard, different parts of the vessel's structure are cutting the Earth's magnetic field at different rates. E.M.F.s induced in the ship's structure cause electric currents to flow and the magnetic fields associated with these "eddy" currents may cause deviations of the compass. Lenz's law states that the magnetic fields which develop will be such as to oppose the motion causing them. Thus if a vessel is swinging to starboard (right-handed) magnetic fields will develop with a polarity which attempts to swing the ship to port (left-handed) and the compass card will in fact be deflected in this sense. For a ship swinging to port (left-handed) the compass card would be deflected right-handed.

Gaussin error is therefore Westerly for a vessel swinging to starboard and Easterly for a vessel swinging to port. While the swing continues the name of the deviation is constant thus giving a similar effect to coefficient A. The eddy currents will die out and the error will become zero within a few minutes of a vessel coming onto a steady course.

When a vessel is swung to adjust compasses it is necessary to keep the ship's head steady on each heading for a few minutes before the deviation is observed to ensure that it is not distorted by Gaussin error.

**Retentive error.** When a vessel steers a steady course for some considerable time the vibration of the ship and the influence of the Earth's magnetic field combine to cause a gradual magnetic change in part of a vessel's hard iron. If the vessel then changes course, this change in the magnetism will initially be retained, but will gradually decay. Magnetism of this type is known as sub-permanent magnetism and the error it gives rise to is known as retentive error. If, as in figure (1) below, a vessel steers a steady Northerly course for an extended period the vessel's sub-permanent magnetism will acquire a red pole forward. If the vessel then alters course to port the red pole will be temporarily retained and will cause Easterly deviation (2). If the vessel alters course to starboard the retained red pole will cause Westerly deviation (3). The deviation caused in this way is similar in name to that due to Gaussin error for alterations of course less than 180°. The difference is that Gaussin error is due to an unsettling of the ship's induced magnetism due to the actual swinging of the ship in azimuth whilst retentive error is due to sub-permanent magnetism developed while the vessel is steering a steady course. The effect of Gaussin error is quickly lost when a vessel steadies on a new course but the effect of retentive error is only lost over a longer period of time.

Retentive error also differs from Gaussin error in that, if a vessel continues to alter course through 360°, the name of the deviation will change in a semi-circular manner thus giving an effect similar to coefficient B and/or C. Thus in the case illustrated below, the fore and aft sub-permanent magnetism induced on a Northerly heading would cause Westerly deviation on Easterly courses and Easterly deviation on Westerly courses (similar to coeff. −B) irrespective of whether the ship altered course to port or to starboard to come on to those headings.

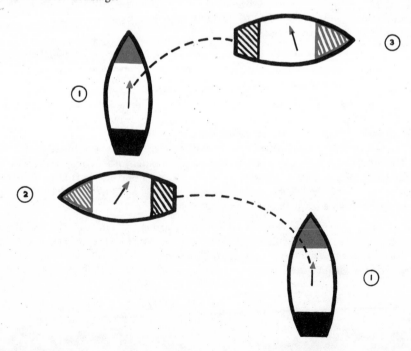

**Beall's compass deviascope** is a model designed to simulate the magnetic effect which may be expected at the compass position aboard ship. A compass is provided on the model, and it is arranged by means of permanent magnets and soft iron rods that a variety of disturbing magnetic fields may be introduced to affect the compass. The model is used to instruct and test students in the methods of correcting a compass and for this purpose a number of permanent magnets are provided together with a "Flinder's bar" and two soft iron spheres. The compass is mounted on a heavy wooden board shaped to represent the deck of a ship. The board is pivoted on a stand so that it may be swung in azimuth and also tilted to simulate the heeling of a ship. A pointer which moves with the board indicates the magnetic direction of the "ship's" head on a dumb card marked on the stand. For instructional purposes it is important that a method of correcting the Deviascope should as nearly as possible follow the comparable method of correcting a ship's compass.

The following procedures are suggested:-

**Tentative method of Deviascope correction**

1.  The model should first be headed East or West by compass and the Flinder's bar placed in a position to correct an estimated $3°$ or $4°$ of coefficient induced B.

2.  The spheres should be shipped in position at about the centre of the brackets as an approximate correction for coefficient D. Bearings of a distant object should be observed on headings of both East and West by compass and the mean of these may be taken as the magnetic bearing for comparing with compass bearings to correct subsequent deviations.

3.  Head the model North or South by compass. Heel the model to port or starboard and remove heeling error by placing vertical permanent magnets in the heeling error "bucket" below the compass bowl. Alternatively, correction of heeling error may be made by means of a vertical force instrument with the deviascope upright on a heading of East or West magnetic.

4.  To correct coefficient B, observe the deviation with the model upright on East or West magnetic. Correct this deviation by inserting fore and aft magnets on either side of the deviascope deck.

5.  To correct coefficient C, head the model North or South magnetic and observe the deviation. Correct this by inserting athwartships magnets on the deviascope "deck" forward and abaft the compass position.

6.  To correct coefficient D, head the model on an intercardinal point and adjust the position of the spheres to remove any deviation observed.

7.  Head the model on the remaining cardinal points and a remaining intercardinal point adjacent to the first and if any appreciable deviation is found on a particular heading, remove half of it by adjusting the appropriate corrector.

8.    Swing the model again on at least eight equidistant points of the compass and make a table of the deviations found.

## Deflector method of deviascope correction

The deviascope deflector consists of a permanent magnet of constant magnetic moment. The magnet, when at right angles to the meridian, causes a deflection which varies inversely as the directive force. This should be compared with the Kelvin deflector which achieves a constant deflection by means of a variable magnetic moment, the corresponding reading varying directly as the directive force.

1.    Head East by compass and place Flinder's bar forward to correct 3° or 4° of induced B.

2.    Place spheres at centre of brackets as an estimated correction for coefficient D.

3.    Correct heeling error as for the tentative method, but it should be noted that the deflector method of correction is used when it is supposed impossible to observe a magnetic direction and if a vertical force instrument is used the model should be steadied on East or West by compass as an approximation to East or West magnetic.

4.    Head North by compass, place the deflector magnet in position with the blue end over compass North, rotate the deflector through 90° and read the deflection of the compass card.

5.    Head East by compass, use the deflector turned in the same sense as above and again note the deflection.

6.    Head South by compass, use the deflector as above and note the deflection. Whilst remaining on this heading, correct coefficient B by inserting fore and aft magnets on the deviascope "deck" on either side of the compass until a deflection is achieved which is the mean of the original deflections on North and South.

7.    Head West by compass, make a deflection as before and with the instrument again untouched correct coefficient C by inserting athwartships magnets on the deviascope "deck" either forward or abaft the compass position to achieve the mean of the original deflections on East and West.

8.    Calculate the mean of the deflections on North, South, East and West and correct coefficient D by adjusting the position of the spheres until this deflection is achieved with the model still heading West.

A table of residual deviations cannot be made up after a deflector swing because it is assumed that there is no means of observing a magnetic bearing available. The accuracy of the adjustment may, however, be assessed by comparing headings of the model by compass with the corresponding magnetic headings as indicated on the dumb-card on the deviascope stand.

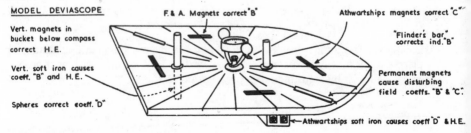

MODEL DEVIASCOPE

F. & A. Magnets correct "B"

Athwartships magnets correct "C"

Vert. magnets in bucket below compass correct H.E.

Vert. soft iron causes coeff. "B" and H.E.

Spheres correct coeff. "D"

"Flinder's bar" corrects ind. "B"

Permanent magnets cause disturbing field coeffs. "B" & "C".

Athwartships soft iron causes coeff "D" & H.E.

**Degaussing.** Magnetic mines are designed to respond to changes in the local magnetic field as a ship passes over them. The changes in the vertical magnetic field at a particular depth due to the passage of a ship can be recorded to form what is known as the ship's magnetic signature. The principle of degaussing is to fit a number of very large coils in a ship and to pass currents through the coils so that a magnetic field is produced beneath the ship equal to but opposite to the ship's signature. If this balance could be perfectly achieved there would be no fluctuation in the local magnetic field at the designed depth as the ship passed overhead. This book is not concerned with the detailed techniques of degaussing but merely with their effect on the compass.

**Compensation.** The magnetic fields associated with degaussing coils affect the permanent magnetism at the compass position and therefore the three components Force P, Force Q and Force R.

Force P causes coefficient B and, to compensate for changes due to degaussing currents, small corrector coils with fore and aft axes ("B" coils) are fitted on each side of the binnacle. The B coils are composed of a number of separate windings. Each winding is associated with a particular degaussing coil so that when a current is supplied to a degaussing coil a proportional current is supplied to the associated windings of the B coil. It is necessary to adjust the proportional control so that the B coils eliminate the fore and aft component of magnetism at the compass position due to the degaussing coils. To achieve this balance, with the ship on any random heading, a magnet is used to make the compass needle lie in the athwartships line. One of the degaussing coils is then switched on and the needle is generally deflected. Finally the proportional control is adjusted until the current in the corresponding windings of the B coils produces a magnetic field which restores the compass needle to the athwartships line. This sequence is followed in turn for each degaussing coil and its associated windings in the B coils until all have been dealt with.

Force Q causes coefficient C. Generally the degaussing coils fitted to ships have no athwartships effect and therefore do not interfere with force Q. Degaussing coils which do affect athwartships magnetism may however be necessary in very large ships and in such cases "C" coils with axes in the athwartships line are fitted to the binnacle. The C coil currents necessary to provide compensation for the magnetic effect of the degaussing coils are found in a similar way to the B coil currents except that the compass needle is set in the fore and aft line before the degaussing coils are switched on in turn so that it is sensitive to deflection by athwartships fields.

Force R is a cause of heeling error and, to compensate for changes due to degaussing currents, a small coil with a vertical axis (heeling error corrector coil) is fitted in the binnacle. Individual windings in the heeling error corrector coil are again associated with particular degaussing coils. The proportional control for the current in each heeling error corrector coil winding is again adjusted separately with only its associated degaussing coil energised. The adjustment is made by levelling a vertical force instrument needle in the compass position, observing its deflection when a particular degaussing coil is switched on and then restoring it to the horizontal by adjusting the current to the associated heeling error corrector coil windings.

Because the vertical field from the heeling error corrector coil induces magnetism in the Flinder's bar it is preferable to complete the adjustment of the heeling error corrector coil before the adjustment of the B coils.

When the compensating arrangements are properly set up, appropriate currents are supplied to the corrector coils whenever the degaussing coils are energised.

# 3. Worked Examples

Notes:- (1) Conventionally Sines are positive for angles from $0°$ - $180°$ and negative for angles from $180°$ - $360°$.

Cosines are positive for angles from $0°$ - $90°$ and $270°$ - $360°$ and negative for angles from $90°$ - $270°$.

(2) Functions of angles from $0°$ - $90°$ may be looked up directly in trigonometrical tables.

Functions of angles from $90°$ - $270°$ are found by entering tables with the difference between the angle and $180°$ and using the appropriate sign.

Functions of angles from $270°$ - $360°$ are found by entering tables with the difference between the angle and $360°$ and again applying the appropriate sign.

Angles greater than $360°$ are dealt with by subtracting $360°$ from the angle before looking up the required function.

**Example 1**. Calculate the deviation on courses of $040°(C)$ and $300°(C)$, given the following values for the coefficients:- A = $-1°$, B = $+2.5°$, C = $-3°$, D = $+2°$ and E = $-1°$.

The basic formula to find the deviation on a heading of $\zeta$ by compass is:-

$$\delta = A + B \sin \zeta + C \cos \zeta + D \sin 2\zeta + E \cos 2\zeta$$

The name of the deviation due to a particular coefficient may be found by taking note of the sign of the coefficient and adhering strictly to the sign convention when the sines and cosines are evaluated. Easterly deviation is conventionally designated as positive and Westerly as negative.

The following diagrams can also be used to find the name of the deviation due to each coefficient on any required heading. They may be used to check the names of the deviations obtained from the sign convention in the lines marked * in the calculation.

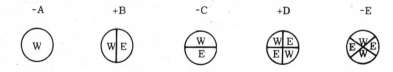

Then on 040°(C):-
$$\delta = -1 + 2.5 \sin 040° - 3 \cos 040° + 2 \sin 080° - 1 \cos 080°$$
$$= -1 + 2.5 \times 0.64 - 3 \times 0.77 + 2 \times 0.98 - 1 \times 0.17$$
$$= -1 + 1.60 - 2.29 + 1.97 - 0.17 \qquad *$$
$$= 0.11 \text{ (i.e. } 0.11°E.)$$

Since positive deviation is conventionally Easterly.

Also on 300°(C):-
$$\delta = -1 + 2.5 \sin 300° - 3 \cos 300° + 2 \sin 600° - 1 \cos 600°$$
$$= -1 + 2.5 \times -\sin 60° - 3 \times \cos 60° + 2 \times -\sin 60° - 1 \times$$
$$\qquad\qquad\qquad\qquad\qquad\qquad\qquad\qquad ' -\cos 60°$$
$$= -1 + 2.5 \times -0.87 - 3 \times 0.5 + 2 \times -0.87 - 1 \times -0.5$$
$$= -1 - 2.16 - 1.5 - 1.74 + 0.5 \qquad *$$
$$= -5.90 \text{ (i.e. } 5.9°W.)$$

Since negative deviation is conventionally Westerly.

**Example 2.** A vessel which is upright is swung through 90° and the following deviations are observed:- on 090°(C), 3°W.; on 135°(C), 2°W.; and on 180°(C), 4°E. Assuming the compass is well sited so that coefficients A and E are zero, find the deviation when heading 250°(C).

In this type of problem it is not possible to make a complete analysis of the deviations. If coefficients A and E are zero however, the deviation on 180°(C) is due to coefficient C only and, since the deviation is East on a Southerly heading, the sign of coefficient C is negative, i.e. Coefficient C = −4°. Similarly, when heading 090°(C), the deviation is only due to coefficient B and, since the deviation is West on an Easterly heading, the sign of co-efficient B is negative, i.e. Coefficient B = −3°. The deviation on 135°(C) is due partly to each of the coefficients B, C and D. Since B and C are known, coefficient D may be calculated by substituting in the equation for the deviation on 135°(C) thus:-

$$\delta = B \sin \zeta + C \cos \zeta + D \sin 2\zeta$$
$$-2 = -3 \sin 135° - 4 \cos 135° + D \sin 270°$$
$$-2 = -3 \times \sin 45° - 4 \times -\cos 45° + D \times -\sin 90°$$
$$-2 = -2.12 + 2.83 - D$$
$$D = 2.71$$

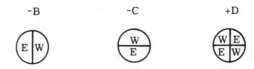

-B              -C              +D

The value of coefficient D calculated above may now be used to find the value of the total deviation on 250°(C).

$$\delta = B \sin 250° + C \cos 250° + D \sin 500°$$
$$= -3 \times -\sin 70° - 4 \times -\cos 70° + 2.71 \sin 40°$$
$$= 2.82 + 1.37 + 1.74$$
$$= 5.93 \text{ (i.e. } 5.93°E.)$$

**Example 3.** During the course of a swing, compass bearings of a star were observed and true bearings calculated as in the table below. Find the variation and the value of the deviation on a heading of 160°(C).

| Compass Course | 000° | 045° | 090° | 135° | 180° | 225° | 270° | 315° |
|---|---|---|---|---|---|---|---|---|
| Compass Bearing | 069° | 064° | 064° | 065° | 063° | 063½° | 071° | 077° |
| True Bearing | 075° | 075½° | 076° | 076½° | 077° | 078° | 079° | 079½° |

The effect of variation is to cause a constant error on all headings of the ship and is thus similar in effect to coefficient A. The value of the variation may be found by analysis by a similar method to that used for finding coefficient A, but the value found in this way will only be the correct variation if coefficient A is zero. The compass error may be used instead of the deviation to calculate the remaining coefficients.

| Comp. Co. | True Brg. | Comp. Brg. | Error | B | C | D | E |
|---|---|---|---|---|---|---|---|
| N. | 075° | 069° | 6° E | | 6° E | | 6° E |
| N.E. | 075½° | 064° | 11½° E | | | 11½° E | |
| E. | 076° | 064° | 12° E | 12° E | | | 12° W |
| S.E. | 076½° | 065° | 11½° E | | | 11½° W | |
| S. | 077° | 063° | 14° E | | 14° E | | 14° E |
| S.W. | 078° | 063½° | 14½° E | | | 14½° E | |
| W. | 079° | 071° | 8° W | 8° W | | | 8° W |
| N.W. | 079½° | 077° | 2½° E | | | 2½° W | |
| | | | 8│80° E | 2│4° E | 2│8° W | 4│12° E | 4│0° |
| | Variation = | | 10° E | 2° E | 4° W | 3° E | 0° |

$$B = +2° \qquad C = -4° \qquad D = +3° \qquad E = 0°$$

On a course of $160°(C)$ the deviation is given as follows:-

$$\delta = A + B \sin \zeta + C \cos \zeta + D \sin 2\zeta + E \cos 2\zeta$$
$$= 0 + 2 \sin 160° - 4 \cos 160° + 3 \sin 320° + 0 \cos 320°$$
$$= 2 \times \sin 20° - 4 \times - \cos 20° + 3 \times - \sin 40°$$
$$= + 2.5°$$

The deviation on $160°(C) = 2.5°E$.

Note:- It is sometimes thought preferable, when making the analysis, to use the compass *errors* to calculate the variation and then to make a separate column of *deviations* for calculating the coefficients as below. There is, of course, no difference in the final result.

| Comp. Co. | True Brg. | Comp. Brg. | Error | Vari-ation | Devi-ation | B | C | D | E |
|---|---|---|---|---|---|---|---|---|---|
| N. | 075° | 069° | 6° E | 10°E | 4° W | | 4°W | | 4°W |
| N.E. | 075½° | 064° | 11½°E | 10°E | 1½°E | | | 1½°E | |
| E. | 076° | 064° | 12° E | 10°E | 2° E | 2°E | | | 2°W |
| S.E. | 076½° | 065° | 11½°E | 10°E | 1½°E | | | 1½°W | |
| S. | 077° | 063° | 14° E | 10°E | 4° E | | 4°W | | 4°E |
| S.W. | 078° | 063½° | 14½°E | 10°E | 4½°E | | | 4½°E | |
| W. | 079° | 071° | 8° E | 10°E | 2° W | 2°E | | | 2°E |
| N.W. | 079½° | 077° | 2½°E | 10°E | 7½°W | | | 7½°E | |

$8|80°$ E      $2|4°E$   $2|8°W$   $4|12°$ E   $0°$

Variation = $\underline{10°\ E}$      $\underline{2°E}$   $\underline{4°W}$   $\underline{3°E}$

$$B = +2° \quad C = -4° \quad D = +3° \quad E = 0$$

**Example 4.** If the deviation due to hard iron in a ship is $10°W.$ when heading $090°(C)$, at a position (1) where $H = 20$ amperes per metre $(A/m)$, find the deviation due to the same iron:- (a) when on the same heading at a position (2) where $H = 16$ amperes per metre $(A/m)$ and (b) when heading $315°(C)$ at a position where $H = 30$ amperes per metre $(A/m)$.

The deviation due to this iron comprises coefficient permanent B and since Westerly deviation is caused on an Easterly course it is named negative. The deviation varies inversely as H and directly as the sine of the compass course.

-B   $\left(\text{E} \middle| \text{W}\right)$

a) Comparing the deviation at positions 1 and 2,

$$\frac{\delta_2}{\delta_1} = \frac{H_1}{H_2} \times \frac{\sin \zeta_2}{\sin \zeta_1}$$

$$\frac{\delta_2}{-10} = \frac{20}{16} \times \frac{\sin 90°}{\sin 90°}$$

$$\delta_2 = -10 \times \frac{20}{16} \times \frac{1}{1}$$

$$= -12.5 \text{ (i.e. } 12.5° \text{ W)}$$

b) Comparing the deviation at positions 1 and 3,

$$\frac{\delta_3}{\delta_1} = \frac{H_1}{H_3} \times \frac{\sin \zeta_3}{\sin \zeta_1}$$

$$\frac{\delta_3}{-10} = \frac{20}{30} \times \frac{\sin 315°}{\sin 90°}$$

$$\delta_3 = -10 \times \frac{20}{30} \times \frac{-0.707}{1}$$

$$= 4.7 \text{ (i.e. } 4.7° \text{ E)}$$

Note:- The name of the deviation, as given by the sign convention, may be checked by observing that in the diagram for −B above the required heading of 315° lies in the semi-circle containing Easterly deviation.

**Example 5.** The deviation due to coefficient induced B is 6°E, when heading 225°(C) at a position (1) where the angle of dip is +60°. Find the deviation when heading 302°(C) at a position (2) where the angle of dip is +20°.

The deviation on a Westerly course at position (1) is named East and the sign of coefficient B is therefore negative.

−B   $\left(\text{E} \middle| \text{W}\right)$

It is clear from the diagram that the name of the deviation on a course of 302°(C) will still be East. The value of the deviation due to coefficient induced B varies directly as the sine of the compass course and directly as the tangent of the dip. The sign of the answer to the calculation should indicate the name of the deviation independently.

$$\frac{\delta_2}{\delta_1} = \frac{\sin \zeta_2}{\sin \zeta_1} \times \frac{\tan \theta_2}{\tan \theta_1}$$

$$\frac{\delta_2}{6} = \frac{\sin 302° \times \tan 20°}{\sin 225° \times \tan 60°}$$

$$\delta_2 = 6 \times \frac{-\sin 58° \times \tan 20°}{-\sin 45° \times \tan 60°}$$

$$= \underline{1.5 \text{ (i.e. } 1.5° \text{ E)}}$$

Deviation when heading $302°$ (C) at position (2) is $\underline{1.5° \text{ E}}$

**Example 6.** Permanent B is $+8°$ and induced B is $-4°$ at a position (1) where H = 30 A/m and Z = 40 A/m. Find the deviation due to these coefficients when heading $255°$(C) at a position (2) where H = 20 A/m and Z = $-30$ A/m.

At (1) We have permanent + B       At (1) We have induced – B

$$+ \text{B} \quad \left(\text{W} \middle| \text{E}\right) \qquad\qquad - \text{B} \quad \left(\text{E} \middle| \text{W}\right)$$

This varies inversely as H       This varies as $\dfrac{Z}{H}$

$$\frac{\delta_2}{\delta_1} = \frac{H_1}{H_2} \qquad\qquad \frac{\delta_2}{\delta_1} = \frac{Z_2}{H_2} \times \frac{H_1}{Z_1}$$

$$\frac{\delta_2}{8} = \frac{30}{20} \qquad\qquad \frac{\delta_2}{-4} = \frac{-30}{20} \times \frac{30}{40}$$

$$\delta_2 = \frac{8 \times 30}{20} \qquad\qquad \delta_2 = \frac{-4 \times -30 \times 30}{20 \times 30}$$

$$= \underline{12} \qquad\qquad\qquad = \underline{4.5}$$

Note:- At position (2) Z is negative so that the polarity in the ship's vertical soft iron is reversed with the change from Northern to Southern hemisphere and the sign of induced B is also reversed

At (2) we have induced       + B   $\left(\text{W} \middle| \text{E}\right)$

Since permanent B and induced B are both positive at position (2) the required course of $225°$ falls into the Westerly semi-circle in each case, thus providing a check on the name of the answer.

At position (2) Total Coeff. B = Permanent B + Induced B

$$= 12° + 4.5°$$
$$= 16.5°$$

Deviation due to Coeff. B on 255°(C) = B sin ζ

$$= 16.5 \times \sin 255°$$
$$\equiv 16.5 \times - \sin 75°$$
$$= -15.9 \text{ (i.e. } 15.9°W)$$

**Example 7.** At position (1) on the magnetic equator, (H = 30 A/m) the deviation on a heading of 090°(C) was 6°W. At position (2) of Ushant (H = 20 A/m, Dip = +65°) the deviation on a heading of 090°(C) was 8°W. Find the value of permanent B and induced B at the second position.

In this example it is necessary to assume that the compass is well placed so that coefficients A and E are both negligible and all the deviation on a heading of 090°(C) may therefore be taken as due to coefficient B.

Where, as in this example, one position of a ship is given as on the magnetic equator, the angle of dip ($\theta$) and the vertical component (Z) of the Earth's magnetic field are known to be zero and the value of induced B is also zero. The deviation at the first position is thus due entirely to coefficient permanent B and this may be varied inversely as the horizontal component (H) of the Earth's magnetic field to find the value of permanent B at the second position.

To find permanent B at (2)    $\dfrac{\delta_2}{\delta_1} = \dfrac{H_1}{H_2}$                    Permanent

$$\dfrac{\delta_2}{-6} = \dfrac{30}{20}$$                    $-B$

$$= \dfrac{-6 \times 30}{20}$$

$$= \underline{-9}$$

| | | | |
|---|---|---|---|
| Total coefficient B at (2) | $= -8°$ | | Induced |
| Permanent  " " " " | $= \underline{-9°}$ | | |
| Induced  " " " " | $= \underline{+1°}$ | | $+B$ |

Permanent B = $-9°$                    Induced B = $+1°$

**Example 8.** At a position (1) where H= 30 A/m Dip = 55° a total coefficient B of +6° was observed with no correctors in place. At a position (2) where H = 25 A/m Dip = −64° a total coefficient B of +2° was observed. What correction should be made at the second place with permanent magnets and what correction should be made by means of the Flinder's bar?

In order to correct the permanent part of coefficient B by means of fore and aft magnets and the induced part of coefficient B by means of the Flinder's bar it is necessary to split total coefficient B into its component parts. This may be done by solving two simultaneous equations.

Let $\chi$ = permanent B at the second position
and y = induced     "  "   "     "         "

Then at (2) $\chi + y = +2$ ............................. ①

At position (1), Permanent B $= \chi \times \dfrac{H_2}{H_1} = \chi \times \dfrac{25}{30} = 0.83\chi$

At position (1), Induced B $= y \times \dfrac{Tan\,\theta_1}{Tan\,\theta_2} = y \times \dfrac{Tan\,55°}{-Tan\,64°} = -0.7y$

and at (1),      $0.83\chi - 0.70y = +6$ ........................... ②
            $0.83\chi + 0.83y = 1.66$ ...................... ③     (Multiplying (1) by 0.83)
                 $- 1.53y = 4.34$              (Subtracting (3) from (2))

$$y = \frac{-4.34}{1.53}$$

$$y = \underline{-2.84°}$$

Substituting in ① $\chi + y$     $= 2$
            $\chi - 2.84$   $= 2$
                 $\chi$     $= \underline{4.84°}$

Permanent fore and aft magnets should be placed in the binnacle to correct the 4.84° of permanent B when the ship is heading East. Since coefficient permanent B is positive, the deviation will be Easterly when the ship is heading East and the magnets should be placed with red ends forward.

The Flinder's bar should be placed to correct 2.84° of induced B when the ship is heading East. Since coefficient induced B is negative the deviation will be Westerly when the ship is heading East and the Flinder's bar (which has a red pole on top in the Southern hemisphere) should be placed abaft the compass position.

**Example 9.** At position (1) where H = 20 A/m, Z = 40 A/m, a vessel's compass is corrected to achieve zero deviation with the Flinder's bar forward of the compass and fore and aft magnets inserted in the binnacle with red ends forward. At position (2) where H = 30 A/m, Z = 20 A/m, a coefficient B of +3° was observed. How should the correctors be readjusted at the second position? What would be the value of coefficient B at a third position (3) where H = 20 A/m, Z = −25 A/m if the correctors were not readjusted?

In this type of question, coefficient B must again be split into its component parts and, since the readjustment is to be made at the second position, it is here that $\chi$ and y are put to represent the permanent and induced components respectively.

At (2)                     $\chi + y$     $= +3$ ................................. ①

At position (1) Permanent B     $= \chi \times \dfrac{H_2}{H_1} = \chi \times \dfrac{30}{20} = 1.5\chi$

At position (1) Induced B      $= y \times \dfrac{Z_1}{H_1} \times \dfrac{H_2}{Z_2} = y \times \dfrac{40}{20} \times \dfrac{30}{20} = 3y$

At (1), since compass is corrected,  $1.5\chi + 3y \quad = 0$ .......... ②
$$1.5\chi + 1.5y = 4.5 \text{ ......... ③} \quad \text{(Multiplying ① by 1.5)}$$
$$1.5y = -4.5 \quad \text{(Subtracting ③ from ②)}$$
$$y = -3°$$

Substituting this value in (1),  $\chi + y = 3$
$$\chi - 3 = 3$$
$$\chi = \underline{6°}$$

The fore and aft magnets in place in the binnacle with red ends forward are causing a −B. Since a +B is calculated, these magnets must be undercompensating and should be moved closer to the compass until the +6° of permanent B is eliminated.

In the Northern hemisphere the Flinder's bar forward of the compass has a blue pole on top and causes a +B. Since a −B is calculated, the Flinder's bar is also undercompensating and should be increased in length until the −3° of induced B is eliminated.

To find the value of coefficient B at the third position if the correctors are not readjusted, the permanent and induced components must be treated separately.

Permanent B at (3)    $= 6 \times \dfrac{H_2}{H_3} = 6 \times \dfrac{30}{20} = +9$

Induced B at (3)    $= -3 \times \dfrac{-Z_3}{H_3} \times \dfrac{H_2}{Z_2} = -3 \times \dfrac{-25 \times 30}{20 \times 20} = +5.6$

Induced B at (3)    $= +5.6°$
Permanent B at (3)    $= \underline{+9.0°}$

Total B at (3)    $= \underline{+14.6°}$

**Example 10.** At a position (1) where H = 20 A/m, Z = 40 A/m, coefficient B was found to be $+2°$ and coefficient C $+6°$. Both coefficients were then corrected with permanent magnets. At a position (2) where H = 40 A/m, Z = 0, coefficient B was found to be $+3°$ and coefficient C, $-1°$. How should the compass have been corrected at the first position?

To correct the coefficients properly at the first position it is necessary to split them into permanent and induced components. This may conveniently be achieved by noting that the second position is on the magnetic equator and the deviations there are due to permanent effects only. These permanent effects can be varied inversely as H to calculate the permanent components at the first position as follows:-

Permanent B, ship and magnets at (2) $= +3°$      Permanent C, ship and magnets at (2)

                                                         $= -1°$

Permanent B, ship and magnets at (1) $= 3 \times \dfrac{H_2}{H_1}$ Permanent C, ship and magnets at (1)

                            $= 3 \times \dfrac{40}{20}$                      $= -1 \times \dfrac{H_2}{H_1}$

                                                       $= -1 \times \dfrac{40}{20}$

                                     $= 6°$                           $= -2°$

Magnets cause                    $= \underline{-2°}$      Magnets cause        $= \underline{-6°}$
Permanent B, ship alone          $+8°$       Permanent C, ship alone $+4°$
Coefficient B, ship alone        $\underline{+2°}$        Coeff. C, ship alone    $\underline{+6°}$
Induced B, ship alone            $\underline{-6°}$        Induced C, ship alone   $\underline{+2°}$

Fore and aft magnets should have been placed with red ends forward to correct a permanent B of $+8°$.

Athwartships magnets should have been placed with red ends to starboard to correct a permanent C of +4°.

The Flinder's bar should have been placed to correct an induced B of −6° and an induced C of +2°. It would be necessary to slew the Flinder's bar for this purpose and, to find the angle of slew:-

$$\text{Tan M} = \frac{\text{Induced C}}{\text{Induced B}} = \frac{2}{6} = \frac{1}{3}$$

$$\underline{M = 18\frac{1}{2}°}$$

The Flinder's bar would have to be placed forward of the compass to correct −B, and to port to correct +C. To correct both coefficients it should therefore be placed on the port bow and slewed 18½° from the centre line.

The maximum deviation which will be corrected by the Flinder's bar in its slewed position will be such that:-

$$\delta = \sqrt{(\text{Induced B})^2 + (\text{Induced C})^2}$$
$$\delta = \sqrt{6^2 + 2^2}$$
$$\delta = 6.3°$$

This maximum deviation will occur on such a heading of the ship that the Flinder's bar in its slewed position will lie East or West from the compass, i.e. N.71½°W. or S.71½°E. The correction for induced B and induced C should therefore have been made with the ship on one of these headings.

**Example 11.** In the English Channel (1) the deviation due to coefficient D was observed to be 4°E. when heading 110°(C). Find the deviation due to the same cause off Cape Town (2) when heading 030°(C).

Coefficient D is unaffected by change of magnetic latitude or change of hemisphere and varies only as the sine of twice the compass course. Comparing deviations at (1) and (2):-

$$\frac{\delta_2}{\delta_1} = \frac{\sin 2\zeta_2}{\sin 2\zeta_1}$$

$$\delta_2 = \frac{\delta_1 \sin 2\zeta_2}{\sin 2\zeta_1}$$

$$= \frac{4 \sin 60°}{\sin 220°}$$

$$= \frac{4 \sin 60°}{-\sin 40°}$$

$$= -5.4° \;\; (\text{i.e. } 5.4° \text{ W})$$

−D

Since Easterly deviation is initially caused on a South-easterly course, coefficient D is named negative. The name of the deviation on 030°(C) may be checked by noting that this heading lies in a quadrant of the −D diagram containing Westerly deviation.

**Example 12.** During a swing through 90°, with the vessel heeled constantly 5° to port, the following deviations were observed:- On S., 4°E., on S.W., 2°E., on W., 2°W. Assuming that coefficient A and E are zero, find the deviation when heading 340°(C).

Since there is no coefficient A or E, the deviation when heading South by compass is due to coefficient C and to heeling error. These effects cannot be separated, but they both vary as the cosine of the compass course and they can be treated as a single effect provided that the angle of heel does not change, and named as for coefficient C.

$$(C + H. E.) = -4°$$

− C

Since there is no coefficient A or E, the deviation when heading West by compass is due only to coefficient B.

$$B = 2°$$

+ B

On a heading of S.W. by compass the deviation is due to a combination of effects:-

$$\delta = B \sin \zeta + (C + H. E.) \cos \zeta + D \sin 2 \zeta$$

substituting known values,

$$2 = 2 \sin 225° - 4 \cos 225° + D \sin 450°$$
$$2 = -1.4 + 2.8 + D$$
$$D = 2 + 1.4 - 2.8$$
$$D = 0.6 \qquad + D$$

All the necessary quantities are now known to calculate the deviation on any other heading and on 340°(C):-

$$\delta = B \sin \zeta + (C + H.E.) \cos \zeta + D \sin 2 \zeta$$
$$= 2 \sin 340° - 4 \cos 340° + 0.6 \sin 680°$$
$$= -0.7 - 3.8 - 0.4$$
$$= -4.9 \text{ (i.e. } 4.9° \text{ W)}$$

Deviation on a heading of 340°(C) is 4.9°W.

**Example 13.** Two soft iron spheres are attached to a binnacle to correct an estimated coefficient +D. They are placed athwartships to correct a maximum deviation of 7°. Later, with the spheres still in position, the ship is swung, and a coefficient D of −2° and a coefficient E of −2½° are observed. How should the position of the spheres be adjusted?

Coefficient D of ship and spheres together   = −2°
"   " "   "   " spheres alone   = −7°
"     " " ship alone     = + 5°

The spheres in their original position are clearly overcompensating and should be moved outwards on their brackets to correct 5° instead of 7°. To correct for coefficient E, the spheres are slewed from their athwartships position through an angle given by:-

$$\text{Tan } 2M = \frac{E}{D}$$
$$= \frac{2½}{5}$$
$$= ½.$$
$$2M = 26½°$$
$$M = 13¼°$$

To correct, coefficient −E alone, the spheres should be shipped in a line from 4 points on the starboard bow to four points on the port quarter, and the spheres must be slewed from the athwartships line towards this position, i.e. the starboard sphere should be forward and the port sphere abaft the athwartships line.

The maximum deviation to be corrected by the spheres in the slewed position $= \sqrt{D^2 + E^2}$

$$= \sqrt{5^2 + 2\frac{1}{2}^2}$$

$$= 5.6°$$

The maximum deviation will occur on directions of the ship's head such that the spheres in their slewed position lie in the N.E. − S.W. line or the N.W. − S.E. line, i.e. 058¼°(C), 148¼°(C), 238¼°(C) and 328¼°(C). These four headings are 90° apart by compass. The position of the spheres may be adjusted on any one of them.

**Example 14.** During a swing through 360°, the following deviations were observed on intercardinal headings:- N.E. = 5°E., S.E. = 2°W., S.W. = 1°E., N.W. = 4°W. The spheres were then placed on their brackets 40cm. apart and equidistant from the compass. Coefficients B and C were properly corrected and the deviation on N.E. was then observed to be 1°W. How should the spheres be readjusted to eliminate this deviation? Coefficient A may be assumed to be negligible.

To find the original value of coefficient D, the deviations on the intercardinal points should be added (the names of the deviation on S.E. and N.W., being reversed) and the sum divided by 4.

$$D = \frac{5°E + 2°E + 1°E + 4°E}{4}$$

$$= \frac{12° E}{4}$$

$$= 3° E \qquad\qquad +D$$

| Coefficient D of ship alone on N.E. | = | = 3° E. |
|---|---|---|
| " " " ship and spheres on N.E. | | = 1° W. |
| " " " spheres alone " " | | = 4° W. |

The spheres are overcompensating when 40cm. apart and must be moved outwards on their brackets so that they cause 3°W. instead of 4°W. The effect of a corrector varies inversely as the cube of its distance from the compass.

$$\frac{d_2^3}{d_1^3} = \frac{\delta_1}{\delta_2}$$

$$\frac{d_2^3}{40^3} = \frac{4}{3}$$

$$d_2^3 = 40^3 \times \frac{4}{3}$$

$$d_2 = 40 \sqrt[3]{\frac{4}{3}}$$

$$d_2 = \underline{44 \text{ cm.}}$$

Distance between the spheres should be <u>44 centimetres.</u>

**Example 15.** A fore and aft magnet is placed in a binnacle 48 centimetres from the compass needles and causes 4°E. deviation when heading East by compass. When heading 230°(C) the deviation due to coefficient B is observed to be 1°E. How should the magnet be moved to compensate for this?

The deviation due to coefficient B varies as the sine of a vessel's compass course. Thus on 230°(C):-

$$\delta = B \sin 230°$$
$$1 = B \times - \sin 50°$$
$$B = -1 \operatorname{cosec} 50°$$
$$B = -1.3°$$

To check the name of this result it may be noted that since the deviation on a course in the Westerly semi-circle is named East, coefficient B is negative.

| | | |
|---|---|---|
| Coefficient B of ship and magnet | = | −1.3° |
| "       " due to magnet | = | +4.0° |
| "       " of ship alone | = | −5.3° |

The magnet is undercompensating when 48 centimetres from the compass and should be moved closer (raised in the binnacle) to cause +5.3° instead of +4.0°. The effect of the magnet varies inversely as the cube of the distance from the compass, Thus:-

$$\frac{d_2^3}{d_1^3} = \frac{\delta_1}{\delta_2}$$

$$\frac{d_2^3}{48^3} = \frac{4}{5.3}$$

$$d_2 = 48 \sqrt[3]{\frac{4}{5.3}}$$

$$\underline{d_2 = 43.8 \text{ cm.}}$$

The magnet should be moved 4.2 centimetres closer.

**Example 16.** The deviation due to heeling error is 5°W. on a course of 140°(C) when heeled 10° to starboard. What will be the deviation on a course of 070°(C) when heeled 5° to port?

The deviation due to heeling error varies directly as the angle of heel and directly as the cosine of the compass course. Conventionally, starboard angle of heel is named positive and port angle of heel is named negative.

$$\frac{\delta_2}{\delta_1} = \frac{i_2}{i_1} \times \frac{\cos \zeta_2}{\cos \zeta_1}$$

$$\frac{\delta_2}{-5} = \frac{-5}{10} \times \frac{\cos 70°}{\cos 140°}$$

$$\delta_2 = \frac{-5 \times -5 \times \cos 70°}{10 \times -\cos 40°}$$

$$= \underline{-1.1° \text{ (i.e. } 1.1° \text{ W.)}}$$

Note that:- The name of the deviation changes with change of heel from starboard to port and also with change of course from the Southern semi-circle to the Northern semi-circle. The name of the deviation in the second condition thus remains Westerly. Alternatively it can be noted that the deviation on the first course is towards the low side. Deviation towards the low side on the second course clearly gives rise to Westerly deviation. These arguments check the name of the deviation obtained by using the sign convention above.

Deviation on the second course = 1.1°W.

**Example 17.** At a certain position where the variation is 16°W., the deviation due to heeling error was observed to be 9°E. when heeled 6° to port on a course of 035°(C). If the other coefficients are properly corrected, calculate the compass course to steer to make good a course of 104°(T) when heeled 8° to port.

The deviation due to heeling error varies directly as the angle of heel and directly as the cosine of the compass course. In this case however, the second compass course is not known and the magnetic course must be used as a first approximation. Having thus calculated an approximate deviation an approximate compass course is found and this may then be used to calculate a more accurate deviation.

Starboard angles of heel are again taken as positive and port angles of heel are named negative.

| | |
|---|---|
| True course to steer | 104° |
| Variation | 16°W. |
| Mag. Course = Approximate Compass Course | 120° |

For approximate deviation on 2nd course:-

$$\delta_2 = \delta_1 \times \frac{i_2}{i_1} \times \frac{\cos \zeta_2}{\cos \zeta_1}$$

$$= 9 \times \frac{-8}{-6} \times \frac{\cos 120°}{\cos 35°}$$

$$= \frac{9 \times -8 \times -\cos 60°}{-6 \times \cos 35°}$$

$$= -7.3° \text{ (i.e. 7.3° W.)}$$

This deviation is to the high side and changes name as the course changes from Northerly to Southerly, thus confirming that its name is Westerly.

| | | |
|---|---|---|
| Approximate deviation | = | 7.3° W. |
| Required Mag. course | = | 120.0° |
| Approx. Comp. course | = | 127.3° |

Repeating the above calculation using this compass course instead of the magnetic course:-

$$\delta_2 = \frac{9 \times -8 \times \cos 127.3°}{-6 \times \cos 35°}$$

$$= -8.9 \text{ (i.e. 8.9° W.)}$$

| | | |
|---|---|---|
| Deviation | = | 8.9° W. |
| Required magnetic course | = | 120.0° |
| Comp. Course to steer | = | 128.9° |

**Example 18.** At a position (1) in North latitude, H = 30 A/m, Z = 40 A/m, and heeling error was observed to be $6°$E. when heeled $10°$ to port. This error was corrected by vertical magnets placed 40cm. below the compass needles. At a position (2) in South latitude, H = 20 A/m, Z = −30 A/m, the heeling error was observed to be $6°$W. when heeled $5°$ to port on the same heading. What alteration should be made in the position of the corrector magnet?

Heeling error consists partly of induced and partly of permanent effects and the correction by permanent magnets therefore remains satisfactory only for one magnetic latitude. The effect of the corrector magnet varies inversely as H and directly as the angle of heel so that comparing the deviation it causes at positions (1) and (2).

$$\frac{\delta_2}{\delta_1} = \frac{H_1}{H_2} \times \frac{i_2}{i_1}$$

$$\frac{\delta_2}{-6} = \frac{30}{20} \times \frac{-5}{-10}$$

$$\delta_2 = \frac{-6 \times 30 \times -5}{20 \times -10}$$

$$= \underline{-4\tfrac{1}{2}°}$$

Note that the magnet must cause $6°$W. to correct the heeling error at position (1) and with no change of course or heel it will cause deviation of the same name at position (2).

At position (2) Corrector magnet causes $4\tfrac{1}{2}°$W.
”   ”   ” ship and magnet    ”   $6°$W.
”   ”   ” ship alone       ”   $1\tfrac{1}{2}°$W.

To correct the compass at position (2) the magnet must cause $1\tfrac{1}{2}°$E. instead of $4\tfrac{1}{2}°$W. The magnet must therefore be reversed end for end and lowered in the binnacle to a new position such that:-

$$\frac{d_2^3}{d_1^3} = \frac{\delta_1}{\delta_2}$$

$$\frac{d_2^3}{40^3} = \frac{4\tfrac{1}{2}}{1\tfrac{1}{2}}$$

$$d_2 = 40\sqrt[3]{3}$$

$$d_2 = \underline{57.6 \text{ centimetres}}$$

**Example 19.** At position (1), H = 20 A/m, Z = 50 A/m, when heading 000°(C) the heeling error was observed to be 4°W. when heeled 8° to starboard. This was corrected with heeling error magnets. At position (2), H = 40 A/m, Z = 0, when heading 180°(C) the heeling error was observed to be 2°E. when heeled 4° to port. This was again removed by adjusting the heeling error magnets. What deviation is to be expected at a position (3), H = 20 A/m, Z = −25 A/m, when heading 000°(C) and heeled 6° to port?

In this type of question the heeling error must be split into induced and permanent components so that the effect at position (3) can be calculated. This can conveniently be achieved by starting from position (2) on the magnetic equator where the heeling error is all permanent and working back to position (1).

Permanent heeling error, ship and magnet, at (2)  $= +2°$

"       "      "      "      "      "      " (1)

$$= 2 \times \frac{H_2}{H_1} \times \frac{i_1}{i_2} \times \frac{\cos \zeta_2}{\cos \zeta_1}$$

$$= \frac{2 \times 40 \times 8 \times 1}{20 \times -4 \times -1}$$

$$= 8 \quad \text{(i.e. } 8° \text{ E.)}$$

Permanent heeling error, ship and magnet at (1) = 8°E.
Total heeling error, ship and magnet, at (1)      = 0°
Induced heeling error at (1)                  = 8°W.

When the heeling error magnet is readjusted on the magnetic equator the permanent component of heeling error is completely compensated by a permanent magnet. The permanent component will thus remain corrected for all latitudes and the heeling error at position (3) will be due only to the induced component. Since the induced component is known at position (1) it can be varied directly as the angle of heel and directly as the tangent of the dip $\left(\frac{Z}{H}\right)$ to find the corresponding deviation at position (3).

Induced heeling error at (1)     $= 8° \text{ W.}$

"       "      "      " (3)     $= -8 \times \dfrac{Z_3}{H_3} \times \dfrac{H_1}{Z_1} \times \dfrac{i_3}{i_1}$

$$= -8 \times \frac{-25}{20} \times \frac{20}{50} \times \frac{-6}{8}$$

$$= -3° \quad \text{(i.e. } 3° \text{ W.)}$$

The deviation is West because with change of hemisphere the induced high side error at (1) becomes low side error at (3).

**Example 20.** Before adjusting a compass by means of a Kelvin Deflector, the Flinder's ba
was placed in position forward of the compass and the spheres were set in an estimate(
position athwartships. State how the correctors should be placed if the following reading
were then taken:-

| Comp. Course | Deflector Reading |
|:---:|:---:|
| 000° | 32.4 |
| 090° | 30.0 |
| 180° | 28.6 |
| 270° | 34.0 |

The Kelvin Deflector reading varies directly as the directive force at the compass position

*Coefficient B.* From the above table, the directive force on 000°(C) is greater than th(
directive force on 180°(C). This effect is caused by a fore and aft magnetic field in th(
ship, directed towards the bow. Such a magnetic field causes Easterly deviation on Easterl(
courses and gives rise to coefficient +B. The correction of coefficient B should be made b(
inserting fore and aft magnets in the binnacle with red ends forward until the deflecto(
reading on 000°(C) or 180°(C) is brought to the mean of the two original readings, i.e(
to 30.5.

*Coefficient C.* From the table, the directive force on 090°(C) is less than the directiv(
force on 270°(C). This effect is caused by an athwartships magnetic field in the ship
directed towards the starboard side. Such a magnetic field causes Easterly deviation o(
Northerly courses, giving rise to coefficient +C. The correction of coefficient +C shoul(
be made by inserting athwartships magnets in the binnacle with red ends to starboar(
until the deflector reading on 090°(C) or 270°(C) is brought to the mean of the tw(
original readings, i.e. 32.0.

*Coefficient D.* The mean directive force on 090° and 270°(32.0) is greater than the mea(
directive force on 000° and 180°(30.5). This effect may be caused by continuous fore an(
aft soft iron or by athwartships soft iron divided about the compass position. Either (o(
both) of these arrangements of soft iron causes Westerly deviation on North-easterl(
courses and gives rise to coefficient −D.

The spheres in position athwartships are causing a −D and are consequently overcomper(
sating. They should be moved outwards on their brackets until the deflector reading o(
any cardinal point of the compass is brought to the mean of all the original readings, i.(
to 31.25.

DIVIDED ATHWARTSHIPS
IRON INCREASES D.F.
ON E. OR W.

CONT. F. & A. IRO
DECREASES D.F.
ON N. OR S.

**Example 21.** On a deviascope model, a Flinder's bar is placed forward of the compass and spheres athwartships. How should the compass be corrected if the following deflections are observed?

| Comp. Course | Deflection |
|:---:|:---:|
| 000° | 20° |
| 090° | 16° |
| 180° | 14° |
| 270° | 22° |

On the deviascope model the angle of deflection varies inversely as the directive force at the compass position so that the larger the angle of deflection the smaller is the directive force.

*Coefficient B.* The directive force on 180°(C) is greater than the directive force on 000°(C). This effect is caused by a magnetic field directed towards the stern, giving rise to Westerly deviation on Easterly courses and thus to coefficient −B. The correction should be made by placing fore and aft magnets with red ends aft on the deviascope deck on either side of the compass until the deflection on either 000°(C) or 180°(C) is brought to the mean of the two original readings, i.e. to 17°.

*Coefficient C.* The directive force on 090°(C) is greater than the directive force on 270°(C). This effect is caused by a magnetic field directed towards the port side, giving rise to Westerly deviation on Northerly courses and thus to a coefficient −C. The correction should be made by placing athwartships magnets with red ends to port on the deviascope deck forward and abaft the compass position until the deflection on either 090°(C) or 270°(C) is brought to the mean of the two original readings, i.e. to 19°.

*Coefficient D.* The mean of the directive force on 000°(C) and 180°(C) is greater than the mean of the directive force on 090°(C) and 270°(C). This effect may be caused by fore and aft horizontal soft iron divided about the compass position or by continuous athwartships soft iron. Either (or both) of these effects cause coefficient +D. The spheres in position athwartships are causing a −D and are consequently undercompensating. They should be moved inwards on their brackets until the deflection on any of the cardinal points of the compass is brought to the mean of all the original readings, i.e. to 18°.

**Example 22.** A magnetised needle, free to vibrate in a horizontal plane, is placed in the compass position of a ship. Find the name of coefficients B, C and D, and the value of lambda if the time taken for the needle to make 10 complete vibrations is observed on directions of the ship's head as follows:-

| Mag. Co. | Comp. Co. | Time |
|----------|-----------|------|
| 000°     | 354°      | 27 secs. |
| 090°     | 094°      | 25 secs. |
| 180°     | 186°      | 23 secs. |
| 270°     | 266°      | 21 secs. |
| Ashore   |           | 20 secs. |

The strength of the magnetic field, and hence the directive force, at the compass position varies inversely as the square of the time of one oscillation of the needle ($H \propto \frac{1}{T^2}$) The faster the needle vibrates the stronger must be the strength of the field.

*Coefficient B.* The directive force on 000° is less than the directive force on 180°. This is due to a magnetic field at the compass position directed towards the stern and such a field causes coefficient $-B$.

*Coefficient C.* The directive force on 270° is greater than the directive force on 090° This is due to a magnetic field at the compass position directed towards the starboard side and such a field causes coefficient $+C$.

*Coefficient D.* The mean directive force on 000° and 180° is smaller than the mean on 090° and 270°. This may be due to divided athwartships soft iron or continuous fore and aft soft iron giving rise in either case to coefficient $-D$.

*Lambda* is the ratio of the mean directive force towards magnetic North aboard to the directive force ashore. The vibrating needle is acted upon by a magnetic field directed towards compass North and the effect of this when heading due North, East, South and West can be denoted by $H_n$, $H_e$, $H_s$, $H_w$, respectively. (The directive force towards magnetic North ashore being denoted by H).

These magnetic fields are inversely proportional to the square of the corresponding times of vibration:-

$$H_e \propto \frac{1}{T_e^2} \qquad H_s \propto \frac{1}{T_s^2} \quad \text{and ashore } H \propto \frac{1}{T^2}$$

The directive force towards *magnetic North* is equal to the directive force towards *compass North* multiplied by the cosine of the deviation. Thus the directive force towards magnetic North when heading East:-

$$H_e \cos \delta_e \propto \frac{1}{T_e^2} \cos \delta_e$$

Comparing the directive force aboard ship on each heading with the directive force ashore:-

$$\frac{H_n \cos \delta_n}{H} = \frac{T^2}{T_n^2} \cos \delta_n = \frac{20^2}{27^2} \cos 6° = 0.55$$

$$\frac{H_e \cos \delta_e}{H} = \frac{T^2}{T_e^2} \cos \delta_e = \frac{20^2}{25^2} \cos 4° = 0.64$$

$$\frac{H_s \cos \delta_s}{H} = \frac{T^2}{T_s^2} \cos \delta_s = \frac{20^2}{23^2} \cos 6° = 0.75$$

$$\frac{H_w \cos \delta_w}{H} = \frac{T^2}{T_w^2} \cos \delta_w = \frac{20^2}{21^2} \cos 4° = 0.90$$

| | |
|---|---|
| Sum of the four ratios | 4 ) 2.84 |
| Mean of four ratios, ($\lambda$) | 0.71 |

Lambda = 0.71

*Note.* In the above calculation, T is strictly the time for one oscillation of the needle and each of the times given is for ten oscillations. Clearly, it is unnecessary to divide each of the given times by ten since this would make no difference to the ratios. If the number of vibrations timed has been different in each case, it would have been necessary to use the time of one vibration when making the comparison above.

**Example 23.** At a certain position (1) where H = 30 A/m, Z = 20 A/m, a vertical force instrument is balanced ashore with the weight at 10 divisions on the South arm. If the ship's multiplier is 0.8, where should the weight be placed to correct heeling error with the vertical force instrument in the compass position at (a) position (1) and (b) at position (2) where H = 20 A/m, Z = −30 A/m?

(a)    To correct heeling error at position (1),

the reading aboard   = reading ashore × ship's multiplier.

= 10 × 0.8

= 8 divisions

(b) At the second position (2) the reading also varies directly as the vertical component (Z) of the Earth's magnetic field, i.e:-

$$\text{reading aboard} = \text{reading ashore} \times \text{ship's multiplier} \times \frac{Z_2}{Z_1}$$

$$= 10 \times 0.8 \times \frac{-30}{20}$$

$$= -12 \text{ divisions}$$

This result is negative because the second position is in the Southern hemisphere and so the weight must be placed on the North arm of the vertical force instrument.

**Example 24.** A vessel has coefficients A, C and E all zero. When heading 064°(C) the deviation is observed to be 4°W. and when heading 207°(C) the deviation is observed to be 6°E. What deviation is to be expected with the vessel heading 315°(C)?

Questions of this type depend upon the equation giving the deviation on any heading:-

$$\delta = A + B \sin \zeta + C \cos \zeta + D \sin 2\zeta + E \cos 2\zeta$$

If only two coefficients are unknown a knowledge of the deviation on two headings is sufficient to write down a pair of simultaneous equations. These can be solved to find the two unknown coefficients. In this example only coefficients B and D are present so that for any heading:- $\quad \delta = B \sin \zeta + D \sin 2\zeta$

On 064°(C): $\qquad -4 = B \sin 064° + D \sin 128°$

$\qquad\qquad\qquad -4 = 0.9\,B + 0.62\,D \qquad\qquad\qquad$ .... ①

On 207°(C): $\qquad\quad 6 = B \sin 207° + D \sin 414°$

$\qquad\qquad\qquad\quad 6 = -0.45\,B + 0.81\,D \qquad\qquad$ .... ②

Multiplying ② by 2: $\quad 12 = -0.9\,B + 1.62\,D \qquad\qquad$ .... ③

Adding ① and ③ $\qquad\quad 8 = 2.24\,D$

$$D = \frac{8}{2.24}$$

$$D = 3.57°$$

Substituting for D
in ① : $\qquad\qquad\qquad -4 = 0.9\,B + 0.62 \times 3.57$

$\qquad\qquad\qquad\qquad -4 = 0.9B + 2.21$

$\qquad\qquad\qquad 0.9\,B = -6.21$

$\qquad\qquad\qquad\quad B = -6.9°$

On 315°(C): $\qquad\qquad \delta = B \sin 315° + D \sin 630°$

$\qquad\qquad\qquad\qquad = -6.9 \times -\sin 45° + 3.57 \times -\sin 90°$

$\qquad\qquad\qquad\qquad = 4.88 - 3.57$

$\qquad\qquad\qquad\qquad = 1.31 \text{ (i.e. } 1.31°E)$

Deviation when heading 315°(C) is 1.31°E.

**Example 25.** A vessel has coefficients A, B, D and E all zero. When heading 060°(C) and heeled 6° to starboard the deviation was observed to be 2°E. When heading 143°(C) and heeled 9° to port the deviation was observed to be 8°E. Find the value of coefficient C and state what heeling error is to be expected when heading 299°(C) and heeled 10° to starboard.

In this example the deviations observed are due only to coefficient C and to heeling error. These effects both vary as the cosine of the compass course but differ in that heeling error also varies directly as the angle of heel.

Let H represent the deviation due to heeling error on 060°(C) with 6° of starboard heel. Then the deviation due to heeling error on 143°(C) with 9° of port heel is:-

$$H \times \frac{i_2}{i_1} \times \frac{\cos \zeta_2}{\cos \zeta_1}$$

$$= H \times \frac{-9}{6} \times \frac{\cos 143°}{\cos 060°}$$

$$= H \times \frac{-9}{6} \times \frac{-\cos 37°}{\cos 60°}$$

$$= \underline{2.4\ H}$$

Equations for the deviation on 060° (C) and 143° (C) may now be written down in terms of H and coefficient C.

On 060° (C):     2   = C cos 060° + H
                 2   = 0.5 C + H ....................................... ①

On 143° (C):     8   = C cos 143° + 2.4H
                 8   = −0.8 C + 2.4 H ............................ ②

Multiplying 1 by 2.4     4.8 = 1.2 C + 2.4 H ...................... ③

Subtracting ③ from ②     3.2 = −2.0 C

$$C = \frac{3.2}{-2}$$

$$\underline{C = -1.6°}$$

Substituting for C in ①     2 = 0.5 × −1.6 + H

$$\underline{H = 2.8°}$$

Heeling error when heading 299° (C) and heeled 10° to starboard is given by:-

$$H \times \frac{i_2}{i_1} \times \frac{\cos \zeta_2}{\cos \zeta_1}$$

$$= 2.8 \times \frac{10}{6} \times \frac{\cos 299°}{\cos 060°}$$

$$= \frac{2.8 \times 10 \times \cos 61°}{6 \times \cos 60°}$$

$$= \frac{2.8 \times 10 \times 0.48}{6 \times 0.5}$$

$$= 4.5° \quad (\text{i.e. } 4.5° \text{ E.})$$

Coefficient C = −1.6°                Required heeling error = 4.5° E.

**Example 26.** In a vessel heading 050° by the steering compass it is noted that the heading by the standard compass is 047°. A star bearing 245° true is observed from the standard compass to be bearing 257° and the variation is known to be 7° West. Find the deviation of the standard and the steering compasses if it is known that the lubber's line on the steering compass is displaced 1° to starboard of the ship's fore and aft line.

To find the deviation of the standard compass:-

| | |
|---|---|
| Bearing of star | 245°(T) |
| " " " | 257°(C) |
| Error | 12°W. |
| Variation | 7°W. |
| Deviation | 5°W. |

It is advisable to check the comparison with the steering compass by means of a sketch as below:-

| | |
|---|---|
| Ship's head by standard compass | 047°(C) |
| Standard compass deviation | 5°W. |
| Ship's head magnetic | 042°(M) |

The lubber's line of the steering compass is displaced 1° to starboard relative to the direction of the ship's head. Therefore at the steering compass:-

Magnetic direction of lubbers line  043°(M)

Compass direction of lubbers line  050°(C)

Deviation of steering compass        7°W

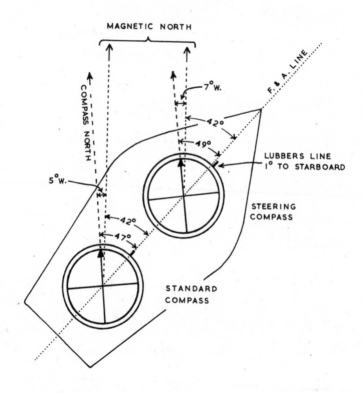

# 4. Formulæ

## Gyro Compass

Rate of Tilting in Degrees per hour = 15 sin Azimuth cos latitude

Rate of Drifting in Degrees per hour = 15 sin lat (where axis is horizontal)

Rate of Precession $P = \dfrac{T}{SI}$ where $T$ = Applied Torque

$\qquad\qquad\qquad\qquad\qquad\qquad S$ = Rate of Spin

$\qquad\qquad\qquad\qquad\qquad\qquad I$ = Moment of Inertia of Rotor

Course Latitude and speed error in degrees = $\dfrac{\text{Speed of Ship} \times \text{Cos. course}}{5\pi \times \text{Cos. latitude}}$

## Magnetic Compass

| | | |
|---|---|---|
| Coefficent A | | $\delta$ is constant |
| " | Permanent B | $\delta \propto \dfrac{1}{H} \times$ sin. comp. co. |
| " | Induced B | $\delta \propto \dfrac{Z}{H} \times$ sin. comp. co. |
| | or | $\delta \propto \text{Tan } \theta \times$ sin. comp. co. |
| " | Permanent C | $\delta \propto \dfrac{1}{H} \times$ cos. comp. co. |
| " | Induced C | $\delta \propto \dfrac{Z}{H} \times$ cos. comp. co. |
| " | D | $\delta \propto$ sin. 2 comp. co. |
| " | E | $\delta \propto$ cos. 2 comp. co. |

Angle of Slew (M) of Flinders' Bar, $\text{Tan } M = \dfrac{\text{Ind C}}{\text{Ind B}}$ $\qquad$ Max. Dev. $= \sqrt{B^2 + C^2}$

" " " (M) of Spheres, $\text{Tan } 2M = \dfrac{E}{D}$ $\qquad$ Max. Dev. $= \sqrt{D^2 + E^2}$

Permanent Heeling Error $\qquad\qquad \delta \propto \dfrac{1}{H} \times$ angle heel $\times$ cos. comp. co.

Induced Heeling Error $\qquad\qquad \delta \propto \dfrac{Z}{H} \times$ angle of heel $\times$ cos. comp. co.

Total deviation:-

$\delta = A + B$ sin. comp. co. $+ C$ cos. comp. co $+ D$ sin 2 comp. co. $+ E$ cos. 2 comp. co.

$\lambda = \dfrac{\text{Mean directive force towards magnetic N. aboard ship}}{\text{Directive force towards magnetic N. ashore}}$

$\mu = \dfrac{\text{Vertical force aboard ship}}{\text{Vertical force ashore}}$  Scale reading on vertical force instrument $=$ Reading ashore $\times \mu_2$

D. F. towards Mag. N. $=$ D.F. towards Comp. N. $\times$ Cos $\delta$

$H \propto \dfrac{1}{T^2}$  for a vibrating needle  $\delta \propto \dfrac{1}{d^3}$  when adjusting corrector

# INDEX